Questions and Answers

The Gospel of Mark

Questions and Answers

The Gospel of Mark
Mike Freze

BAKER BOOK HOUSE
Grand Rapids, Michigan 49516

Copyright 1988
by Baker Book House Company

ISBN: 0-8010-3538-4

Printed in the United States of America

Contents

1 The Twelve Apostles   11

2 Words of Jesus
Sayings, Parables, Beatitudes   23

3 Teachings of Jesus
Laws, Morals, Ethics   34

4 Miracles
Visions, Healings, Appearances   45

5 The Spiritual World
Angels, Demons, The Holy Spirit   57

6 Prophecy
Old and New   68

7 Nature
Earth, Animals, Air   80

8 The Passion   91

9 From Heaven Above
God, Heaven, and Prayer   102

10 General Questions
History, Archaeology, Geography, Unique Features   112

Answers   123

Preface

Many books deal with spiritual questions, are guides for building faith, or offer inspiration. However, I have been unable to find a book which has specific information from the Gospel of Mark in question-and-answer form. A wide variety of information—history, archaeology, geography, and literature—is gathered into this book and the result is a fascinating way to learn and understand more about the Gospel of Mark.

Christians seem to feel that they know something about Jesus' birth, his ministry, his passion, the disciples and their ministry, names and locations of familiar Bible places, and the people who were associated with our Lord's life on earth. But sometimes interesting details are forgotten or overlooked. These details often provide a meaningful background to Bible study.

In order to avoid the predictability of a sentence-by-sentence, question-and-answer format, I have randomly placed the questions under specific categories. This system avoids a book that resembles nothing more than a sequential commentary. Furthermore, this format makes it harder to memorize the answers.

Following the questions on the Gospel of Mark itself is a general section on history, archaeology, geography, and unique features of the Gospels.

Questions and Answers: The Gospel of Mark follows a book on the Gospel of Matthew which was released in April, 1987. I have been deeply grateful for the support and enthusiasm shown by many readers for that initial book. I hope that these questions from the Book of Mark will increase your knowledge about the Lord's life and work.

Because the Gospel of Mark lacks a genealogy prologue and a description of the early years of Jesus, Mary and Joseph, this book begins with the twelve apostles. All other categories covered in Matthew are found here in Mark.

I would like to thank Shirley Morrison, of Deer Lodge, Montana, for her assistance in typing this manuscript. I would also like to thank my family for their encouragement and support.

May the Lord Jesus Christ bring peace and love into your hearts.

Mike Freze

Before You Begin

There are multiple choice options for each question throughout the book. The questions are designated:

> E—easy to answer
>
> M—moderately difficult
>
> H—difficult or hard to solve

Whether long or short, easy or hard, everyone has a 25-percent chance of answering each question correctly. Of course, the multiple choice option does not have to be used if one (or the group) knows the topic or category well.

The multiple choice options are short and specific. Several or all of the options may sound correct or reasonable but there is only one right answer for the question. Few obvious or silly choices are given to prevent the process of elimination from taking over.

Use the King James Version or the New International Version to verify your answers.

I hope you are ready now to challenge yourself in the fascinating world of information from the Gospel of Mark. Enjoy!

Mike Freze

The Twelve Apostles

1. **M** Who was arrested directly before the call of the apostles?
    a. Jesus   b. John the Baptist   c. Matthew   d. Peter
2. **M** What city did the disciples go to immediately after the call of James and John?
    a. Cana   b. Capernaum   c. Nazareth   d. Jerusalem
3. **E** In which physical position did Jesus eat at Matthew's house?
    a. standing   b. sitting   c. reclining   d. walking
4. **M** Besides a tunic, which item of clothing did Jesus allow the disciples to take on their journeys?
    a. sandals   b. money bag   c. an extra tunic
    d. a hat
5. **H** Which disciples were called "sons of thunder"?
    a. Peter, Andrew   b. Philip, Bartholomew
    c. Philip, Andrew   d. James, John
6. **M** Where did Jesus teach the apostles about his coming passion?
    a. near Jerusalem   b. in Jerusalem
    c. the River Jordan   d. at Cana
7. **E** Where did Jesus reveal the end times to the apostles?
    a. Mount of Olives   b. Jerusalem
    c. Capernaum   d. Mount Nebo

8. **E** How did Jesus' clothes appear to the apostles at the transfiguration?
   a. bloodied   b. brilliant red   c. transparent
   d. brilliant white

9. **E** How many loaves did the apostles have to feed the four thousand?
   a. 2   b. 4   c. 6   d. 7

10. **H** How many days' wages would it take for the apostles to feed the five thousand?
    a. 30   b. 100   c. 200   d. 300

11. **M** How did Judas die?
    a. he hanged himself   b. he jumped off a cliff
    c. he was shot   d. it doesn't say

12. **E** What would the apostles be able to handle after Jesus left for heaven?
    a. Romans   b. swine   c. serpents
    d. the Sanhedrin

13. **M** How many apostles did the risen Jesus reveal himself to at the dinner table?
    a. 2   b. 4   c. 11   d. 12

14. **E** Who instructed the women at the tomb to tell Peter that Jesus had risen?
    a. Salome   b. the Virgin Mary
    c. Mary Magdalene   d. an angel

15. **E** Who said, "I do not know the man you are talking about"?
    a. Peter   b. John   c. Andrew   d. Thomas

16. **M** Besides Peter, who else saw Jesus transfigured?
    a. James   b. John   c. James, John
    d. James, Andrew

17. **E** Who did Jesus claim was the greatest of the apostles?

    a. Peter   b. John   c. James   d. the least

18. **M** Which apostle later remembered the curse of Jesus?

    a. Peter   b. John   c. Andrew   d. James

19. **H** Where did the apostles go immediately after Jesus taught in the synagogue?

    a. Peter's house   b. John's house
    c. Joseph's house   d. the Sea of Galilee

20. **E** By what other name was Matthew known?

    a. Thaddaeus   b. Alphaeus   c. Levi   d. Simon

21. **H** What does "Boanerges" mean?

    a. sons of peace   b. sons of thunder
    c. sons of God   d. sons of fishermen

22. **M** Where did Jesus and the apostles go after crossing the Sea of Galilee?

    a. Cana   b. Gerasene   c. Capernaum   d. Nazareth

23. **H** How many different places could the apostles stay in a particular locality?

    a. 1   b. 2   c. as many as possible
    d. it doesn't say

24. **H** On what theme did the apostles question Jesus at a house across the Jordan?

    a. heaven   b. money   c. divorce   d. murder

25. **H** Where did Jesus and the apostles spend the night after entering Jerusalem?

    a. Bethlehem   b. Jerusalem   c. Bethphage
    d. Bethany

26. **M** Which two prophets appeared to the apostles at the transfiguration?
    a. Moses, Elijah   b. Moses, Isaiah
    c. Elijah, Enoch   d. Moses, Jeremiah
27. **E** To which disciple did Jesus ask, "Who am I"?
    a. Peter   b. John   c. Matthew   d. James
28. **M** How did Jesus appear to the apostles after the resurrection?
    a. in a cloud   b. taller   c. the same
    d. changed completely
29. **H** What would the apostles be able to drink after Jesus left for heaven?
    a. blood   b. poison   c. wine   d. fruit juice
30. **H** How many times did Jesus find Peter, James, and John asleep at Gethsemane?
    a. once   b. twice   c. three times   d. not once
31. **M** Where were the disciples headed when Jesus walked on water?
    a. Nazareth   b. Cana   c. Sepphoris   d. Bethsaida
32. **M** Which apostle said, "We have put aside everything to follow you"?
    a. James   b. John   c. Peter   d. Andrew
33. **H** To which apostles did Jesus give the signs of the end times?
    a. Peter, John, Andrew
    b. Peter, John, James, Andrew
    c. John, James, Andrew   d. Philip, Andrew, James
34. **M** What did Peter want to erect at the transfiguration?
    a. temple   b. booths   c. an ark   d. a synagogue

35. **M** Where did Jesus and the apostles go to escape the crowds of Capernaum?
    a. Nazareth   b. the River Jordan
    c. the mountains   d. other villages

36. **E** Whom did James and John abandon to follow Jesus?
    a. Baal   b. Peter and Andrew   c. Alphaeus
    d. Zebedee

37. **E** Who gave Simon the name *Peter*?
    a. Jesus   b. Peter   c. Peter's parents
    d. Peter's mother-in-law

38. **E** How did Jesus send his apostles out to preach?
    a. separately   b. two-by-two   c. all together
    d. it doesn't say

39. **M** What type of places did the busy apostles long to go?
    a. villages   b. deserted places   c. cities
    d. the sea

40. **E** How did Peter identify Jesus?
    a. the Messiah   b. the Christ   c. the Prophet
    d. Elijah

41. **H** How many booths did Peter want to erect at Jesus' transfiguration?
    a. 1   b. 2   c. 3   d. none

42. **H** How many disciples fetched the ass for Jesus' entry into Jerusalem?
    a. 1   b. 2   c. 3   d. none

43. **E** Why did the apostles not question Jesus on his predicted resurrection?
    a. fear   b. lack of faith   c. faith
    d. he didn't mention it

44. **M** Who said, "Master, how good it is for us to be here"?
    a. John   b. James   c. Matthew   d. Peter
45. **E** How many apostles went forth to preach about the risen Jesus?
    a. 4   b. 10   c. 11   d. 12
46. **E** What were the apostles first instructed to do after the risen Jesus left?
    a. repent   b. exorcize   c. heal   d. preach
47. **E** Who brought the news to the apostles that Jesus had risen?
    a. Mary Magdalene   b. the Virgin Mary
    c. Peter   d. Peter, James, John
48. **E** Where did the apostles see Jesus transfigured?
    a. on the water   b. on a mountain
    c. in the desert   d. in Jerusalem
49. **H** By what title did Peter address Jesus at the transfiguration?
    a. Jesus   b. Christ   c. Master   d. Messiah
50. **E** What did the apostles throw on the back of the ass that Jesus rode?
    a. cloaks   b. a blanket   c. sandals   d. money bag
51. **E** After Peter and Andrew were called by Jesus, when did they follow him?
    a. immediately   b. in three days
    c. after John's call   d. six months later
52. **E** Where was Jesus when the disciples couldn't find him?
    a. the mountains   b. the desert
    c. Joseph's house   d. the synagogue
53. **H** Which disciple fasted regularly early in his calling?
    a. Peter   b. John   c. James   d. Matthew

54. **M** How many tunics were the apostles allowed to carry on their journeys?
    a. 1   b. 2   c. 3   d. none

55. **E** Which disciple was James' brother?
    a. Philip   b. Thaddaeus   c. John
    d. Bartholomew

56. **M** Whom did Jesus refer to in defending the disciples' work on the Sabbath?
    a. Moses   b. David   c. Abraham   d. Noah

57. **H** Which apostles wanted to be on Jesus' right and left at his glory?
    a. Peter, John   b. John, Thomas   c. Peter, James
    d. John, James

58. **E** What did the apostles see Jesus cursing?
    a. an adulteress   b. a snake   c. a fig tree
    d. a home

59. **E** When the apostles were in great demand, which necessity did they often miss?
    a. being with friends   b. bathing   c. prayer
    d. eating

60. **E** Which symbol came to the apostles at the transfiguration to show God's presence?
    a. a cloud   b. lightning   c. a dove   d. rain

61. **M** What accompanied the apostles when they preached the risen Jesus?
    a. doubts   b. signs   c. women   d. regrets

62. **H** Which apostle was not present with the risen Jesus?
    a. Judas   b. James   c. Thomas   d. it doesn't say

63. **M** How many of the apostles were first to see Jesus risen?
    a. 2   b. 4   c. 5   d. 12

64. H What building did the disciples go to immediately after the call of James and John?
    a. James' house   b. John's house
    c. the synagogue   d. Peter's house

65. E Which apostle found Jesus in prayer when he escaped the crowds?
    a. Peter   b. John   c. Andrew   d. James

66. E Who joined Matthew, Jesus, and the other disciples for dinner at Matthew's house?
    a. the Sadducees   b. Mary and Joseph
    c. the scribes   d. tax collectors

67. H Which part of the boat was Jesus on when the disciples crossed the sea?
    a. the side   b. the stern   c. the front
    d. the middle

68. H Which disciples were nicknamed "Boanerges"?
    a. James, John   b. Peter, Andrew
    c. Philip, Bartholomew   d. Philip, Thaddaeus

69. E Why did Jesus want his disciples to prepare a boat for him?
    a. he loved fishing   b. he wanted to pray
    c. to avoid the crowds   d. he hated Galilee

70. M On what theme did the apostles begin their preaching?
    a. the kingdom   b. healing   c. repentance
    d. the end times

71. H What was the first miracle performed by Jesus in the presence of an apostle?
    a. changing water to wine   b. physical healing
    c. transfiguration   d. exorcism

72. **M** Who was on James' and John's boat besides their father?
a. their mother   b. hired help   c. friends
d. nobody

73. **E** In what district did Jesus call the first apostles?
a. Peria   b. Judea   c. Galilee   d. Idumea

74. **H** What parable was the first that the disciples questioned?
a. the mustard seed   b. the tenants
c. the fig tree   d. the seed

75. **M** In Capernaum, what were the apostles arguing about?
a. Jesus   b. healings   c. sin   d. who was important

76. **H** Where did the apostles go after feeding the four thousand?
a. the Decapolis   b. Sepphoris   c. Dalmanutha
d. Nazareth

77. **M** How many baskets of leftovers did the apostles have after feeding the four thousand?
a. 5   b. 7   c. 10   d. 12

78. **E** At the transfiguration, whose voice was heard from a cloud?
a. Moses'   b. Elijah's   c. God's   d. Gabriel's

79. **H** Which apostles said that they could share the same pain as Jesus?
a. Peter, John   b. John, Matthew
c. Matthew, Peter   d. James, John

80. **E** What acceptance did the apostles preach as necessary for salvation?
a. baptism   b. love   c. healing   d. exorcism

81. **M** Where did Jesus first appear to some apostles after the resurrection?
    a. in the country   b. in Jerusalem
    c. in Bethany   d. the Mount of Olives

82. **H** For how many days had the crowd of four thousand not eaten?
    a. 1 day   b. 2 days   c. 3 days   d. 5 days

83. **H** Which apostle questioned Jesus about non-apostles exorcizing people?
    a. Peter   b. John   c. James   d. Matthew

84. **E** Which came first: the baptism, healings, the temptation, or the call of the apostles?
    a. healings   b. the baptism   c. the calling
    d. the temptation

85. **H** How did Jesus find James and John?
    a. he saw them   b. Peter led him
    c. Andrew led him   d. by revelation

86. **M** Where were the twelve disciples chosen?
    a. a mountain   b. the desert   c. Capernaum
    d. Jerusalem

87. **M** Which item did Jesus allow the disciples to take on their journeys?
    a. the Scriptures   b. money   c. food   d. a walking stick

88. **M** What did Jesus use to sleep on while the disciples crossed the sea?
    a. a blanket   b. a rock   c. a cushion   d. nothing

89. **H** At which time did Jesus and the apostles arrive in Jerusalem?
    a. early morning   b. noon   c. late afternoon
    d. early evening

90. E By what name did Jesus call Peter when Peter questioned him?

 a. false prophet   b. betrayer   c. Satan   d. faithless

91. M What would believers be able to do after Jesus left for heaven?

 a. exorcize, speak in tongues   b. heal
 c. discern, exorcize   d. a and b

92. E What was the initial reaction of the apostles on hearing of Jesus' resurrection?

 a. belief   b. disbelief   c. fear   d. anger

93. M Which title did James and John use for Jesus?

 a. Messiah   b. Christ   c. Teacher   d. Master

94. E Where did the risen Jesus go immediately after appearing to all the apostles?

 a. Galilee   b. Jerusalem   c. Mount of Olives
 d. heaven

95. H How many disciples accompanied Jesus into Peter's house?

 a. 2   b. 3   c. 4   d. none

96. H When did Jesus suggest crossing the Sea of Galilee by boat?

 a. morning   b. afternoon   c. early evening
 d. late evening

97. E Who decided on the members of the twelve apostles?

 a. Jesus   b. Peter   c. Peter and Andrew
 d. all who wanted to follow

98. E What were the disciples doing immediately after Jesus' burial?

 a. eating   b. preaching   c. healing   d. weeping

99. **M** In the storm on the Sea of Galilee, when did the winds die down?
   a. when Jesus prayed
   b. when Jesus walked on water
   c. when Jesus got into the boat
   d. when the apostles believed

100. **H** How many different times did Judas speak to Jesus?
   a. once   b. twice   c. three times   d. not once

Words of Jesus
Sayings, Parables, Beatitudes

1. **H** What is the first parable in Mark?
   a. the tenants   b. the yeast   c. the seed
   d. the treasure

2. **M** Where was the crowd at the teaching of the parable of the seed?
   a. near the shore   b. on a boat
   c. on a hillside   d. in the city

3. **E** In whom did Jesus first confide God's mysterious reign?
   a. the women   b. the Gentiles   c. the sinners
   d. the twelve apostles

4. **H** In the parable of the tenants, what did the planter put around the vineyard?
   a. a hedge   b. a stone wall   c. a grain field
   d. nothing

5. **M** According to the seed parable, where in the plant can the bird build its nest?
   a. its roots   b. its shade   c. its hollow
   d. its branch tops

6. **E** What is Mark's shortest parable?
   a. the pearl   b. the mustard seed
   c. the treasure   d. the yeast

7. **E** Whom did Jesus most encourage to come to him?
   a. the sick   b. repenters   c. the poor   d. children

8. **M** Which parable immediately follows the parable of the seed?

   a. the mustard seed   b. the tenants
   c. the pearl   d. divine mercy

9. **M** How many times did Jesus speak to Pontius Pilate?

   a. once   b. twice   c. three times   d. six times

10. **E** Which was the first theme spoken by Jesus to the crowds?

    a. love   b. discipleship   c. God's reign
    d. repentance

11. **E** By which other name does Jesus refer to "hell"?

    a. Hades   b. Gehenna   c. Balaam   d. Gomorrah

12. **E** Which animal can pass through a needle's eye more easily than a rich man can get to heaven?

    a. a horse   b. a camel   c. a donkey   d. a dog

13. **M** In the tenants parable, to where did the landowner journey?

    a. to Tyre   b. neighboring village   c. the city
    d. it doesn't say

14. **E** With faith, what will we be able to drink without harm?

    a. poison   b. blood   c. dirty water   d. salty water

15. **M** Where did Jesus teach the parable of the seed?

    a. the shore   b. a boat   c. a mountain
    d. the temple

16. **H** In the parable of the tenants, what did the planter erect?

    a. an altar   b. a statue   c. a wall   d. a tower

17. **E** According to the parable of the seed, what comes to choke people's faith?

    a. greed   b. sickness   c. lust   d. idolatry

18. **E** Which is the shortest saying of Jesus to an apostle?
    a. "Why you?"   b. "Follow me."
    c. "Know that I Am."   d. "Repent and believe."

19. **M** According to Jesus, which hypocrites could be found at banquets?
    a. the Zealots   b. the Pharisees
    c. the Sadducees   d. the scribes

20. **H** Which theme immediately follows the parable of the tenants?
    a. paying Caesar   b. a healing   c. heaven   d. hell

21. **E** What did Jesus ask for when questioned about tribute to Caesar?
    a. a priest   b. a coin   c. a sword   d. a lawyer

22. **E** Where did Jesus teach at Capernaum on the Sabbath?
    a. the Temple   b. the streets   c. Peter's house
    d. a synagogue

23. **M** In the tenants parable, which person who was loved was sent to the tenants?
    a. the owner's daughter   b. the owner's son
    c. the owner   d. the slave

24. **M** Whom did Jesus call his mother and brothers?
    a. the practicing faithful   b. Mary and James
    c. Mary, James, Joses   d. Mary, James, Jude

25. **E** What is never extinguished in hell?
    a. fire   b. salt   c. pain   d. smoke

26. **E** According to Jesus, what should new wine be poured into?
    a. old vats   b. new skins   c. new vats   d. old skins

27. H Which is the first theme to follow the parable of the seed?
    a. the tenants   b. the mustard seed
    c. divine mercy   d. the pearl

28. H According to Jesus, who liked to show off their robes in public?
    a. the scribes   b. the Sadducees
    c. the Herodians   d. the Zealots

29. E In the parable of the seed, which occupation is mentioned first?
    a. money lending   b. preaching   c. farming
    d. selling

30. H According to the parable of the seed, what makes people's faith falter?
    a. lust   b. persecution   c. greed   d. idolatry

31. M In the tenants parable, what happened to the landowner's son?
    a. he was kidnapped   b. he was cursed
    c. he was killed   d. he died of leprosy

32. E According to the example of the seed parable, what is necessary to receive?
    a. baptism   b. death   c. working   d. giving

33. E About which theme did Jesus respond to Pilate?
    a. kingship   b. blasphemy   c. treason   d. the Law

34. E At Nazareth, where did Jesus teach on the Sabbath?
    a. a house   b. the temple   c. a synagogue
    d. the desert

35. H In which parable is Old Testament Scripture quoted?
    a. the good Samaritan   b. the tenants
    c. the wily manager   d. the yeast

36. **M** Which parable immediately precedes the parable of the mustard seed?

    a. the good Samaritan   b. divine mercy
    c. the seed   d. the prodigal son

37. **E** Which of the senses did Jesus urge the people to use to understand his parables?

    a. sight   b. taste   c. touch   d. hearing

38. **E** With faith, which kind of animal will we be able to handle?

    a. wolves   b. serpents   c. scorpions   d. spiders

39. **M** According to Jesus, from where do wicked designs come?

    a. the heart   b. the mind   c. the soul
    d. bad company

40. **H** According to Jesus, what never dies in hell?

    a. sorrow   b. lice   c. souls   d. worms

41. **M** How long were Jesus' instructions in parables to the crowds?

    a. very short   b. medium   c. short and long
    d. at great length

42. **E** In the parable of the seed, what was the first of Jesus' instructions?

    a. work   b. listen   c. reap   d. pray

43. **M** For whom were the parables of Jesus first designed?

    a. the unbelievers   b. the twelve apostles
    c. the Romans   d. the Pharisees

44. **H** In the parable of the tenants, what did the planter dig out?

    a. a treasure   b. a vat   c. a well   d. a grave

45. **H** What type of sentences does Jesus use to start the parable of the mustard seed?
    a. interrogatory   b. command   c. exclamation   d. interjection

46. **H** In the parable of the tenants, which of the dispatchers mentioned was murdered?
    a. the first   b. the second   c. the third   d. the fourth

47. **E** According to Jesus, what was "at hand"?
    a. Elijah   b. Satan's dominion   c. the end   d. God's reign

48. **M** Who is the second person Jesus spoke to?
    a. John the Baptist   b. Simeon   c. a demoniac   d. the Virgin Mary

49. **H** Which theme directly precedes the parable of the seed?
    a. the temptation   b. a healing   c. the Beatitudes   d. Jesus' family

50. **E** What is the theme of Jesus' first sayings?
    a. hell   b. healing   c. the good news   d. discipleship

51. **M** According to Jesus, who were the people to be guarded against?
    a. the high priest   b. the Zealots   c. the scribes   d. the gentiles

52. **E** According to Jesus, what is to be put on a stand for all to see?
    a. a lamb   b. the Torah   c. a lamp   d. a vase

53. **E** In the parable of the tenants, what did the landowner want from the tenants?
    a. wine   b. wheat   c. oats   d. sheep

54. E Besides the Pharisees, who did Jesus accuse of having undesirable yeast?
    a. Judas   b. the Herodians   c. the Sadducees
    d. Herod

55. E For whom is it particularly hard to enter heaven?
    a. the liars   b. the proud   c. the rich   d. the poor

56. M To whom did Jesus compare undesirable yeast?
    a. the Pharisees   b. Herod   c. the Sadducees
    d. a and b

57. E In which physical position was Jesus when he taught the parable of the seed?
    a. sitting   b. standing   c. kneeling   d. walking

58. E Where did Jesus first speak to the crowds?
    a. Galilee   b. Judea   c. Peria   d. Idumea

59. M Who devoured the savings of poor widows?
    a. the Sadducees   b. the Zealots
    c. the scribes   d. the Pharisees

60. H In which chapter does the first parable appear in Mark?
    a. 1   b. 2   c. 3   d. 4

61. E Which condition allows people to understand the parables?
    a. instruction   b. repentance   c. sacrifice
    d. revelation

62. E In which parable do tenants of the land become significant?
    a. the tenants   b. the yeast   c. divine mercy
    d. the wily manager

63. H Who recited long prayers only for the sake of appearance?
    a. the scribes   b. the Sadducees
    c. the Herodians   d. the Pharisees

64. **H** What is the last parable in Mark?
   a. the prodigal son   b. the seed
   c. divine mercy   d. the tenants

65. **H** Which theme immediately precedes the parable of the tenants?
   a. the transfiguration   b. discipleship
   c. Jesus' authority   d. death

66. **M** In the parable of the tenants, where was the landowner's son dragged after being killed?
   a. to a basement   b. inside the vineyard
   c. outside the vineyard   d. to the cliffs

67. **E** What did Jesus say immediately after being baptized?
   a. "My God"   b. "Sabachthani"   c. "Eli, Eli"
   d. nothing

68. **E** According to Jesus, what makes a man impure?
   a. disease   b. unleavened bread
   c. unsacrificed lamb   d. what comes out of him

69. **H** What should we keep in our hearts to be at peace with others?
   a. love   b. salt   c. honesty   d. humility

70. **E** Which Roman emperor did Jesus call by name?
   a. Caesar   b. Nero   c. Constantine   d. Pilate

71. **M** To which Old Testament person did Jesus refer when teaching about work on the Sabbath?
   a. Solomon   b. Jesse   c. Abraham   d. David

72. **E** For whose sake was Jesus handed over to death?
   a. the Romans   b. the demons   c. Satan
   d. sinners

73. **H** What event immediately follows the parable of the mustard seed?
    a. an exorcism   b. the Last Supper
    c. the transfiguration   d. the calming of the sea

74. **E** How many times did Jesus speak before the Sanhedrin?
    a. once   b. twice   c. three times   d. not once

75. **E** According to Jesus, what is not meant to be hidden from view?
    a. a lamp   b. love   c. secrets   d. sins

76. **M** In the parable of the seed, how does the planter know how his seeds grow?
    a. an angel told him   b. when it's harvest
    c. they bloom   d. he doesn't

77. **H** In the parable of the seed, what is the numerical order of the potential harvest?
    a. 100/60/30 fold   b. 60/100/30 fold
    c. 30/60/100 fold   d. none of these

78. **E** Which parable directly follows the seed?
    a. the mustard seed   b. the yeast
    c. divine mercy   d. the wily manager

79. **E** In the parable of the seed, what devoured some of the seed planted?
    a. goats   b. swine   c. sheep   d. birds

80. **M** How did Jesus always explain God's kingdom?
    a. privately   b. publicly   c. both a and b
    d. it doesn't say

81. **M** Besides God's kingdom, what other image is the parable of the mustard seed likened to?
    a. the heavenly banquet   b. the Last Supper
    c. a bird's nest   d. a fishing net

82. **H** In the parable of the tenants, how many dispatchers were sent to the tenants?
    a. 2   b. 3   c. 4   d. over 4
83. **E** What is Jesus' motive for teaching parables at great length?
    a. for the Gentiles   b. for self-glory
    c. for instruction   d. for scholars
84. **M** How many times did Jesus speak during the way of the cross?
    a. once   b. twice   c. three times   d. not once
85. **E** In villages surrounding Nazareth, what did Jesus mainly do?
    a. teach   b. heal   c. pray   d. fast
86. **E** In the parable of the seed, what caused some seeds to have few roots?
    a. lack of sun   b. lack of soil   c. lack of a tiller
    d. lack of love
87. **E** By what format did Jesus always speak to the crowds?
    a. sayings   b. secrets   c. parables   d. legalisms
88. **M** To what did Jesus accuse the Pharisees of clinging?
    a. astrology   b. human tradition   c. the law
    d. superstition
89. **E** In the parable of the tenants, to whom did the landowner lease his land?
    a. farmers   b. sinners   c. women   d. his sons
90. **E** In the tenants parable, what was the motive for the murder of the son?
    a. revenge   b. power   c. fame   d. inheritance
91. **E** According to Jesus, what will everyone be salted with in hell?
    a. bitter herbs   b. yeast   c. fire   d. nothing

92. **E** In whom should we put our trust?
    a. our conscience   b. our hearts   c. Satan   d. God
93. **M** In the tenants parable, who will destroy the sinful tenants?
    a. the owner   b. the laborer   c. Satan
    d. the neighbor
94. **E** What did the money-changers change the temple into?
    a. a house of witches   b. a house of sorcery
    c. a den of thieves   d. a grave of corpses
95. **H** Which parable did Jesus ask his disciples if they understood?
    a. divine mercy   b. the prodigal son
    c. the seed   d. the pearl
96. **M** In the tenants parable, which of the dispatchers mentioned was sent away empty-handed?
    a. the first   b. the second   c. the third
    d. the fourth
97. **E** What parable emphasizes a vineyard?
    a. divine mercy   b. the seed   c. the tenants
    d. the yeast
98. **M** How did Jesus identify himself to the high priest?
    a. the Prophet   b. the Christ   c. the Messiah
    d. the Son of man
99. **M** How many verses are in Mark's "longer ending"?
    a. 12   b. 16   c. 27   d. 36
100. **H** How many times does Jesus speak to John the Baptist?
    a. once   b. twice   c. four times   d. not once

Teachings of Jesus
Laws, Morals, Ethics

1. **E** "_____ and believe the Gospel!"
   a. share b. repent c. live d. dedicate
2. **M** In Capernaum, where did Jesus teach the crowd?
   a. the streets b. the Temple
   c. the synagogue d. in homes
3. **E** "If any man desires to be first, the same shall be last of all and _____ of all."
   a. servant b. ruler c. forgiver d. doubter
4. **H** Where did Jesus say the worm never dies?
   a. the Sanhedrin b. the earth c. the sea
   d. Gehenna
5. **H** How many Old Testament commandments did Jesus quote to the man who called him "good"?
   a. 1 b. 2 c. 6 d. 10
6. **H** Over which issue did Jesus use the burning bush as an example?
   a. God of judgment b. the God of life
   c. the Holy Spirit d. temptation
7. **M** Who wanted to sit someday at Jesus' right hand?
   a. Peter and John b. Peter c. Judas
   d. James and John

8. **M** To whom did Jesus first teach the greatest commandment?
   a. the scribes   b. the Pharisees
   c. the Apostles   d. Pontius Pilate

9. **H** According to Jesus, who paraded their robes as a boastful sign?
   a. the scribes   b. the Sadducees
   c. the Romans   d. the Apostles

10. **M** Whom did Jesus accuse of stealing the money of widows?
    a. King Herod   b. the Pharisees   c. the scribes
    d. Pontius Pilate

11. **E** Who were the last persons Jesus instructed?
    a. Mary Magdalene   b. the Pharisees
    c. the Romans   d. the apostles

12. **E** If a man gains the whole world, what might he lose?
    a. his kingdom   b. his soul   c. respect
    d. contentment

13. **E** What would some people not taste until they saw God's reign?
    a. death   b. salt   c. milk and honey   d. defeat

14. **H** Where was Jesus when he first taught the apostles about the Passion and resurrection?
    a. Judea   b. Idumea   c. Perea   d. Galilee

15. **H** To whom did Jesus say, "Everyone shall be salted with fire"?
    a. Judas   b. John   c. Matthew   d. Peter

16. **M** What moral point did Jesus address at the crowning of thorns?
    a. lowliness   b. poverty   c. suffering   d. none

17. E What was the risen Christ's main message to the apostles?
    a. heal the sick   b. preach the Gospel
    c. forgive sins   d. none

18. H What cured man first caused Jesus to withdraw to the desert?
    a. a leper   b. a demoniac   c. a blind man
    d. a deaf mute

19. M According to Jesus, who arrogantly honored themselves at banquets?
    a. the scribes   b. the Sadducees
    c. the Herodians   d. a and b

20. M According to Jesus, who recited prayers for the sake of appearance?
    a. the Sadducees   b. the Apostles
    c. the Zealots   d. the scribes

21. E To whom did Pharisees ask whether it is lawful to give tribute?
    a. Pontius Pilate   b. King Herod   c. Baal
    d. Caesar

22. M Over what issue did the Sadducees ask for Jesus' advice?
    a. eternal life   b. judgment   c. the Law
    d. eternal marriage

23. M To whom did Jesus say, "Therefore what God has joined together let man not separate"?
    a. Mary Magdalene   b. the Sadducees
    c. the Pharisees   d. Pontius Pilate

24. E Jesus said, ". . . for with God, all things are _____."
    a. perfect   b. good   c. His   d. possible

25. **M** Where did Jesus teach the parable of the seed?
    a. on a mountain   b. by the sea
    c. in the Temple   d. in the desert

26. **E** Of whom is Jesus ashamed?
    a. the Pharisees   b. all sinners
    c. those ashamed of him   d. no one

27. **E** Where does Jesus first instruct the people?
    a. Galilee   b. Judea   c. Perea   d. Idumea

28. **E** ". . . for whoever is not against us is _____."
    a. an apostle   b. for us   c. blessed   d. well protected

29. **E** To whom did Jesus explain the grounds for adultery?
    a. the apostles   b. a Samaritan
    c. the Sanhedrin   d. his parents

30. **E** Whose inscription was on the coin about which Jesus gave a lesson?
    a. King Herod's   b. Pontius Pilate's   c. Caesar's
    d. Baal's

31. **E** Jesus said, "Have faith in _____."
    a. me   b. God   c. the Law   d. safe keeping

32. **H** Which teachers were Jesus' direct forerunners in Palestine?
    a. the Essenes   b. the scribes
    c. the Sanhedrin   d. the elders

33. **H** According to the crowds, Jesus taught better than whom?
    a. the Sadducees   b. John the Baptist
    c. the rabbis   d. the scribes

34. **M** According to Jesus, what have many people replaced God's commandment with?
    a. tradition   b. self rule   c. paganism   d. idolatry

35. E Where did Jesus mainly want to teach and instruct?
    a. the cities   b. the villages   c. the desert
    d. the mountains
36. E According to Jesus, where is the fire never extinguished?
    a. the soul   b. the heart   c. Gehenna
    d. the body
37. E Over what did the rich man refuse everlasting life?
    a. idolatry   b. possessions   c. repentance
    d. the Law
38. H Over what issue did Jesus say, "Why tempt ye me"?
    a. taxes   b. sinning   c. divinity   d. the Law
39. E What must the Son give as a ransom for many?
    a. his word   b. his pain   c. his life   d. his tears
40. H Who learned that he was not far from God's kingdom?
    a. Thomas   b. John   c. Nicodemus   d. a scribe
41. E "There shall not be left one _____ upon another."
    a. soul   b. stone   c. law   d. debt
42. E "Whosoever shall receive one of such _____ in my name, receiveth me."
    a. a relative   b. God   c. children   d. a friend
43. H Whom did Jesus instruct at the transfiguration?
    a. Peter and John   b. James and John
    c. Peter, James, John   d. all Twelve Apostles
44. M Where must the people of Judea flee when they see the abomination?
    a. the temple   b. the desert   c. the mountains
    d. Egypt

45. E According to Jesus, when will the end times come?
    a. after the rapture   b. in one generation
    c. after three signs   d. no one knows

46. M What did Jesus do before he fed the five thousand?
    a. he fled   b. he taught them
    c. he cured them   d. he prophesied

47. E "... and the two will become one _____."
    a. mind   b. spirit   c. flesh   d. Lord

48. E What is possible with trust?
    a. everything   b. faith   c. spiritual gifts
    d. strength

49. M To whom did Jesus teach that no one marries in heaven?
    a. the Sadducees   b. the Pharisees
    c. the Herodians   d. the Samaritan

50. H Who questioned Jesus about paying taxes to the emperor?
    a. Pharisees   b. Herodians   c. Matthew   d. a and b

51. E "And if thy foot offend thee, _____."
    a. go barefoot   b. cover it   c. cut it off
    d. cease walking

52. H As our example, what did Jesus do to the children?
    a. embraced them   b. blessed them
    c. cured them   d. a and b

53. H What outside of a man can make him impure?
    a. disease   b. women   c. the law   d. nothing

54. M "... all things are possible to him that _____."
    a. forgives   b. believeth   c. loves   d. repents

55. M Whom did Jesus first instruct?
    a. Peter   b. Andrew   c. Peter and Andrew   d. John

56. **H** To what event did the crowds first react concerning Jesus' teaching with power and authority?
    a. baptism   b. an exorcism   c. a wedding
    d. Passover

57. **H** To whom did Jesus give examples about the God of the living?
    a. the Pharisees   b. the Herodians
    c. the Sadducees   d. a and b

58. **M** Jesus said, "No one is _____ except God alone."
    a. good   b. righteous   c. pure   d. compassionate

59. **E** According to Jesus, which apostle will be cursed?
    a. Judas   b. Thomas   c. James the Just   d. none

60. **E** Jesus said, ". . . if any man shall say to you, Lo, here is Christ . . . _____."
    a. thank God   b. follow him   c. believe
    d. believe him not

61. **H** Which theme did Jesus last preach on?
    a. love   b. sin   c. the Law   d. baptism

62. **H** According to Jesus, who arrogantly sat in the front of the synagogues?
    a. the Sadducees   b. the scribes
    c. the Pharisees   d. the Romans

63. **H** Where did Jesus teach about the "Son of David" image?
    a. the temple   b. Bethany   c. Capernaum
    d. the River Jordan

64. **E** "For this cause shall a man leave his _____ and _____ and cleave to his wife."
    a. father, mother   b. brothers, sisters
    c. home, country   d. sin, pride

65. **M** To whom did Jesus say, ". . . For whoever is not against us is for us"?
   a. Peter   b. James   c. John   d. Philip

66. **H** How many times did Jesus teach John the Baptist?
   a. once   b. twice   c. three times   d. not once

67. **H** From whom did Jesus ask for a coin?
   a. the Herodians   b. the Pharisees
   c. the Sadducees   d. a and b

68. **M** What must we keep in our hearts to be at peace?
   a. salt   b. fire   c. yeast   d. Jesus' body

69. **M** "Be not afraid, only _____."
   a. use force   b. have confidence   c. love
   d. believe

70. **E** "The Sabbath was made for _____."
   a. the Father   b. man   c. Jesus   d. the angels

71. **E** Where did Jesus first instruct the apostle Peter?
   a. Jerusalem   b. Sea of Galilee   c. Jericho
   d. Bethany

72. **E** Where was the synagogue in which Jesus most often taught?
   a. Jericho   b. Bethany   c. Cana   d. Capernaum

73. **E** Who warned, "Beware of the scribes"?
   a. Jesus   b. Peter   c. Nicodemus
   d. James the Just

74. **H** How many apostles had been called when Jesus taught at Capernaum?
   a. 1   b. 2   c. 4   d. none

75. **E** ". . . and whosoever shall receive _____, receiveth not _____."
   a. faith   b. truth   c. love   d. me

76. E Jesus said, "But from the beginning of Creation God made them _____ and _____."
   a. three, one   b. holy, just   c. male, female   d. evil, just

77. M How many commandments did Jesus claim to be the greatest?
   a. 1   b. 2   c. 3   d. none

78. H Whom did Jesus say would receive the severest sentence?
   a. the scribes   b. the Romans   c. the Herodians   d. the Zealots

79. M Jesus said, "What I say unto you I say to all, _____."
   a. Repent   b. Watch   c. Cling to faith   d. Pray

80. M Who did Jesus first teach about carrying one's cross?
   a. the crowds   b. the apostles   c. the Sanhedrin   d. a and b

81. E What were the apostles instructed to do at the transfiguration?
   a. tell the Pharisees   b. become transfigured   c. remain silent   d. tell the crowds

82. M What does Jesus teach the Baptist at the River Jordan?
   a. baptism   b. repentance   c. discipleship   d. nothing

83. E What did Jesus mainly come to preach?
   a. good news   b. forgiveness   c. the law   d. discipleship

84. M Where does greed come from?
   a. evil men   b. the law   c. the heart   d. tradition

85. E "How hard it is for the _____ to enter the Kingdom of God!"

   a. sinner   b. rich   c. proud   d. thief

86. M What teaching did Jesus present during the way of the cross?

   a. repentance   b. forgiveness   c. mercy   d. none

87. H To whom did Jesus prove his authority to forgive sins?

   a. the Sadducees   b. the scribes
   c. the crowds   d. no one

88. E According to the story of the fig tree, what will we know is near?

   a. summer   b. winter   c. spring   d. the Antichrist

89. E What must a man deny to follow Jesus?

   a. sin   b. possessions   c. rituals   d. self

90. H To whom did Jesus ask, "Can you drink of the cup that I drink of"?

   a. Peter and James   b. Thomas
   c. James and John   d. Judas

91. E Who on earth has authority to forgive sins?

   a. John the Baptist   b. all the Apostles
   c. Peter   d. Jesus

92. H To whom does Jesus first give instructions?

   a. Peter   b. Andrew   c. John the Baptist
   d. the crowds

93. E What impressed the crowds about Jesus' teaching?

   a. his authority   b. his voice   c. his knowledge
   d. his humility

94. E Where was Jesus teaching when he called Matthew to discipleship?

   a. Bethany   b. Jericho   c. Sea of Galilee
   d. River Jordan

95. E According to Jesus, what was to be poured out for many?
    a. sins   b. wine   c. his blood   d. living water
96. E According to Jesus, what will someday pass away?
    a. earth   b. the heavens   c. hell   d. a and b
97. H According to Jesus, who accepted marks of respect in public?
    a. the apostles   b. the Herodians
    c. the scribes   d. the Zealots
98. E For what will the apostles be hated?
    a. their arrogance   b. Jesus' name
    c. their authority   d. their preaching
99. M Which apostle did Jesus instruct about expelling demons in his name?
    a. John   b. Peter   c. Andrew   d. Bartholomew
100. M Where was Jesus' teaching first recognized as authoritative?
    a. Cana   b. Capernaum   c. Nazareth   d. Jerusalem

Miracles
Visions, Healings, Appearances

1. **E** What is the first miracle that John the Baptist saw?
    a. the sky breaking   b. a healing
    c. a resurrection   d. an angel
2. **E** After Jesus' miracles people said he was possessed by _____.
    a. Elijah   b. an unclean spirit   c. the Spirit
    d. Satan himself
3. **M** What did Jesus put into the deaf man's ears?
    a. mud   b. oil   c. his tongue   d. his fingers
4. **M** Who was seen in the tomb of the risen Jesus?
    a. a young man   b. a young girl   c. Jesus
    d. no one
5. **E** While curing someone, to whom did Jesus say, "What is thy name"?
    a. demons   b. the lame man   c. the deaf girl
    d. the deaf boy
6. **M** Who first spoke to Jesus at a healing?
    a. the Baptist   b. a demon   c. a leper
    d. a blind man
7. **M** What was Jesus doing when the paralytic from Capernaum came?
    a. preaching   b. praying   c. healing   d. sleeping

8. **M** Which non-Jew did Jesus cure?
   a. an Indian   b. an Egyptian   c. a Greek
   d. a Negro

9. **E** How many times did Jesus try to cure the blind man at Bethsaida?
   a. once   b. twice   c. three times   d. four times

10. **H** After many of Jesus' cures King Herod said, "_____ has been raised from the dead."
    a. John the Baptist   b. Elijah   c. Enoch
    d. Beelzebub

11. **E** When did Jesus heal the man with the withered hand?
    a. on the Sabbath   b. at Passover
    c. at the start of Jubilee   d. on Sunday evening

12. **M** Who experienced the first supernatural vision?
    a. an angel   b. Jesus   c. Satan   d. John the Baptist

13. **E** To what did Jesus say, "Peace, be still."?
    a. the wind   b. a demoniac   c. an epileptic
    d. the sea

14. **H** Jesus said, "Do you remember? When I broke the _____ loaves among five thousand?"
    a. 3   b. 4   c. 5   d. 7

15. **M** Where did Jesus go after he walked on the water?
    a. Gennesaret   b. Gadara   c. Cana   d. Sepphoris

16. **M** Whose healing immediately follows that of Peter's mother-in-law?
    a. a leper's   b. demoniacs   c. a deaf-mute's
    d. a lunatic's

17. **H** Which healing story immediately follows the apostles eating on the Sabbath?
    a. a blind woman   b. an exorcism
    c. a withered hand   d. a paralyzed child

18. **M** After which miracles did the people say Jesus was the greatest prophet?
    a. cures   b. the resurrection
    c. the transfiguration   d. the risen appearances

19. **H** Who did Jesus heal after he cured the Greek girl?
    a. a deaf-mute   b. a possessed girl
    c. a possessed boy   d. a fevered girl

20. **E** Who first saw the resurrected Christ?
    a. Peter   b. Peter and John
    c. Mary Magdalene   d. Martha

21. **E** What was the first miraculous appearance seen by the Baptist?
    a. a dove   b. the sky opening   c. God
    d. an exorcism

22. **M** On whom did Jesus have to try twice for a successful cure?
    a. a fevered girl   b. a blind man
    c. a deaf-mute   d. a demoniac

23. **H** How old was Jairus' daughter when Jesus cured her?
    a. 5   b. 6   c. 9   d. 12

24. **E** When did unclean spirits recognize Jesus as God's Son?
    a. when he expelled them
    b. when they touched him
    c. when he cured others   d. when they saw him

25. **M** Where did the majority of Jesus' first healings take place?
    a. Cana   b. Capernaum   c. Nazareth   d. Jerusalem

26. **E** Who had the daughter that was critically ill?
    a. Jairus   b. Simeon   c. the centurion   d. James

27. **H** Who did Jesus cure in the ten cities?

    a. a deaf-mute   b. a demoniac   c. a dead girl
    d. a dead boy

28. **H** Who was with Jesus when he cured Peter's mother-in-law?

    a. John   b. Philip and Peter   c. James and John
    d. Philip and Andrew

29. **E** Who was first to challenge the miracles of Jesus?

    a. Peter   b. Simeon   c. John the Baptist
    d. a demon

30. **E** To whom was God speaking when the Baptist heard his voice?

    a. Jesus   b. the Baptist   c. Satan   d. no one

31. **M** Which miracle immediately follows the feeding of the five thousand?

    a. the risen appearances   b. the transfiguration
    c. walking on water   d. the resurrection

32. **E** When Jesus first chose the apostles, what did he order them to do?

    a. expel demons   b. preach   c. raise the dead
    d. a and b

33. **E** What vision did the apostles think they saw on the Sea of Galilee?

    a. a ghost   b. an angel   c. a demon   d. Jesus

34. **M** Which recipient of a healing was first to disobey Jesus by making it public?

    a. a paralytic   b. a blind man   c. a demoniac
    d. a leper

35. **M** Where did Jesus cure the man with the withered hand?

    a. Peter's house   b. the Sea of Galilee
    c. Bethsaida   d. a synagogue

36. E After which miracle did the people say Jesus was the Baptist?
    a. the voice of God   b. the resurrection
    c. cures   d. the transfiguration

37. H Whose cure immediately precedes the call of Levi?
    a. the lunatic's   b. the paralytic's
    c. the hemorrhage boy's   d. the demoniac's

38. E What kind of profession did the blind Bartimaeus engage in?
    a. begging   b. sorcery   c. farming   d. stealing

39. E Which miracle first established Jesus' authority?
    a. a healed leprosy   b. a healed blindness
    c. an exorcism   d. a cured deaf-mute

40. M What was needed to cure the "dead" daughter of Jairus?
    a. love   b. trust   c. prayer   d. fasting

41. H Who received the last cure in Mark?
    a. Simeon   b. Bartimaeus   c. Peter   d. Jairus

42. H Where did Jesus cure the deaf man with a speech impediment?
    a. Jerusalem   b. the ten cities   c. Gennesaret
    d. Bethsaida

43. E What is the first chapter in Mark to mention a miracle?
    a. the first   b. the second   c. the third
    d. the fifth

44. M What miracle occurred at Gerasa?
    a. the risen Jesus appeared
    b. the transfiguration   c. a deaf man cured
    d. an exorcism

45. M Whose healing directly precedes Peter's mother-in-law's healing?

   a. a demoniac's   b. a leper's   c. a deaf-mute's
   d. a lame man's

46. M How many loaves did the disciples give to the four thousand?

   a. 2   b. 4   c. 5   d. 7

47. M At what time of day did the women first arrive at Jesus' tomb?

   a. early morning   b. midday   c. afternoon
   d. evening

48. E What was the first miraculous vision of John the Baptist?

   a. the sky opening   b. an angel   c. the Spirit
   d. a future prophecy

49. H What miracle occurred after the calming of the sea?

   a. a physical healing   b. an exorcism
   c. the transfiguration   d. the resurrection

50. H Which apostles were allowed to be with Jesus at the cure of Jairus' daughter?

   a. Peter, Andrew, John   b. Peter, James, John
   c. Philip, James, John   d. Peter and John

51. M Jesus told the paralytic to _____.

   a. walk   b. stand up   c. be healed
   d. sin no more

52. H Who did Jesus cure right before he healed the deaf mute in the ten cities?

   a. a lunatic   b. a paralytic   c. a possessed girl
   d. a possessed man

53. E Where did the blind Bartimaeus get cured?

   a. on a hill   b. in a house   c. in a cave
   d. by a road

54. **H** What Jewish group witnessed the paralytic's healing at Capernaum?
   a. the Pharisees   b. the Sadducees
   c. the Herodians   d. the scribes

55. **M** What did the apostles do besides casting out demons and healing the sick?
   a. anointed the sick with oil
   b. raised the dead   c. received visions
   d. prophesied

56. **E** Jesus told the man in the synagogue to stretch out his _____.
   a. foot   b. hand   c. arm   d. head

57. **M** What did Jesus use to cure the blind man at Bethsaida?
   a. spit   b. oil   c. clay   d. water

58. **E** Which of the sick were cured at Gennesaret?
   a. the lepers   b. the lunatics   c. the lame
   d. everyone

59. **M** Which kind of miracle did Jesus perform often in the Galilean synagogues?
   a. exorcisms   b. physical healings
   c. heavenly signs   d. none

60. **E** Which is the first miracle in Mark?
   a. God speaking   b. the sky parting
   c. the Spirit descending   d. an angel appearing

61. **M** Which healing caused Jesus' reputation to spread throughout Galilee?
   a. an exorcism   b. a withered hand   c. hearing
   d. seeing

62. **M** What did Jairus' daughter do after she got up, cured?
    a. she prayed   b. she slept   c. she cried
    d. she ate

63. **E** What did the hemorrhaged woman hope to do for a cure?
    a. touch Jesus   b. touch Jesus' clothes
    c. touch Peter   d. look at Jesus

64. **H** Who was healed directly before the paralytic at Capernaum?
    a. a lunatic   b. a blind man   c. a leper
    d. a demoniac

65. **M** Which non-Jewish person did Jesus heal near Tyre?
    a. a blind man   b. a possessed boy
    c. a possessed daughter   d. a paralyzed girl

66. **M** In which city did Jesus perform his first miracle?
    a. Capernaum   b. Cana   c. Nazareth   d. Bethany

67. **E** Who witnessed the first miracle?
    a. an angel   b. the apostles   c. Jesus
    d. John the Baptist

68. **E** Whose cure made Jesus aware that power had left his body?
    a. the hemorrhaged woman   b. the lame man
    c. the blind girl   d. the deaf boy

69. **E** After which miracles did the scribes say Jesus was possessed by Beelzebub?
    a. his physical healings   b. his raising the dead
    c. his exorcisms   d. none of these

70. **H** Who did Jesus cure by saying, "Ephphatha"?
    a. a paralytic   b. a deaf-mute   c. a lame man
    d. a demoniac

71. **H** Who said, "Jesus, Son of David, have mercy on me."?
   a. Bartimaeus   b. Jairus   c. Theophilus
   d. Cleophilus

72. **M** Which is the second miracle that John the Baptist experienced?
   a. Satan's fall   b. the Spirit   c. God's voice
   d. a healing

73. **M** At which time of day did Jesus rise from the dead?
   a. early morning   b. midday   c. late afternoon
   d. the evening

74. **M** Which leader thought Jesus was the Baptist raised up?
   a. Pontius Pilate   b. King Herod   c. Caiaphas
   d. Herod Antipas

75. **H** How many men carried the paralytic man to Jesus in Capernaum?
   a. 1   b. 2   c. 3   d. 4

76. **M** Which miracle immediately precedes Jesus' walking on water?
   a. curing a demoniac
   b. feeding the five thousand
   c. calming the storm   d. curing a leper

77. **E** Which was the first miraculous healing witnessed by the Baptist?
   a. an exorcism   b. a withered hand
   c. paralysis   d. none

78. **M** Which leader came to visit Jesus because of his cures?
   a. King Herod   b. Pontius Pilate   c. Caiaphas
   d. Caesar

79. **H** Whose cure resulted in Jesus not being able to enter a town openly?
   a. a lunatic's   b. a demoniac's   c. a leper's
   d. a deaf-mute's

80. **E** Where did Jesus retreat after his healings became known?
   a. the mountains   b. the desert   c. Judea
   d. Peter's house

81. **E** What was calmed when Jesus said, "Peace, be still"?
   a. the sea   b. the wind   c. an epilepsy
   d. a demoniac

82. **E** How did Jairus ask Jesus to heal his daughter?
   a. with a word   b. by a touch   c. with a prayer
   d. with a command

83. **M** After which miracle did the people say Jesus was Elijah?
   a. the risen appearances   b. cures
   c. the transfiguration   d. the resurrection

84. **M** Which miracle did Jesus perform before the Baptist?
   a. healing a leper   b. an exorcism
   c. a transfiguration   d. none

85. **H** What does "Talitha, koum" mean?
   a. "Little girl, . . . get up"   b. "Child, be healed"
   c. "Foul spirit, be gone"   d. "Young man, walk"

86. **M** Which cured victim had been to every doctor without being healed?
   a. the ill girl   b. the lame man   c. the lunatic
   d. the hemorrhaged woman

87. **M.** Who was first healed in Mark?
    a. a paralytic   b. a leper   c. a lunatic
    d. a demoniac
88. **E** Who said, "John (the Baptist) has been raised up"?
    a. King Herod   b. Herod Antipas   c. James
    d. Peter
89. **E** After a healing Jesus once said, "Who touched my _____."
    a. eyes   b. hands   c. clothes   d. body
90. **E** Which vision did the apostles see on the Sea of Galilee?
    a. a demon   b. an angel   c. a ghost   d. Jesus
91. **M** Which miracle occurred immediately after Jesus healed the deaf mute at the ten cities?
    a. feeding the five thousand
    b. feeding the four thousand
    c. the transfiguration   d. a healing
92. **E** To whom did Jesus say that his sins were forgiven?
    a. the lunatic   b. the demoniac
    c. the deaf-mute   d. the paralytic
93. **E** Which "sign" did the Pharisees want from Jesus?
    a. a cure   b. Jonah   c. heavenly   d. none
94. **H** Where did Jesus fail to cure someone on the first try?
    a. Gadara   b. Bethany   c. Cana   d. Bethsaida
95. **M** What was multiplied in the first food miracle?
    a. fish   b. bread   c. wine   d. a and b
96. **M** Who exhausted their money for a cure?
    a. the hemorrhaged woman   b. the blind man
    c. the fever boy   d. Jairus for his daughter

97. **E** What "sign" did Jesus give the Pharisees?
    a. an angel's appearance   b. the transfiguration
    c. Jonah   d. none

98. **M** What did Jesus touch after spitting near the deaf-mute?
    a. the ground   b. his eyes   c. his ear
    d. his tongue

99. **H** Where did the first healing take place in Mark?
    a. Bethany   b. the Temple   c. a synagogue
    d. Egypt

100. **E** Which is the last miracle in Mark?
    a. an angel's appearance   b. the ascension
    c. the risen appearances   d. the resurrection

The Spiritual World
Angels, Demons, The Holy Spirit

1. E Which major baptizer was to come after John the Baptist?
    a. Jesus   b. Peter   c. John   d. Zebedee
2. E At which point did the Spirit send Jesus to the desert?
    a. at Satan's call   b. after God spoke
    c. when Jesus was baptized   d. at dawn
3. M In which town did demons first address Christ as "Jesus of Nazareth"?
    a. Cana   b. Jerusalem   c. Capernaum   d. Bethany
4. E Where did Jesus first pray alone?
    a. the Mount of Olives   b. the synagogue
    c. the River Jordan   d. the desert
5. M What was the name of the possessed man's demon at Gerasa?
    a. Gluttony   b. Legion   c. Ruselius   d. Beelzebub
6. H Where did the once-possessed man of Gerasa testify of his healing?
    a. the ten cities   b. all of Galilee
    c. Capernaum   d. Gerasa
7. E. Where was Jesus said to appear after the resurrection?
    a. Cana   b. Galilee   c. the tomb   d. Capernaum

8. E What did the demon do to the possessed boy whenever it seized him?
   a. it smothered him   b. it struck him
   c. it departed   d. it threw him down

9. E What was lacking to heal the possessed mute boy?
   a. authority   b. trust   c. discernment   d. fasting

10. H What is mentioned second in Mark: Satan, angels, demons, or the Spirit?
    a. Satan   b. angels   c. demons   d. the Spirit

11. E In Mark, only one close follower of Jesus was once possessed. Who was it?
    a. Mary Magdalene   b. Nicodemus   c. Simon
    d. Peter

12. H In which town did Jesus perform his last exorcism?
    a. Jerusalem   b. Bethsaida   c. Capernaum
    d. Gerasa

13. E Besides chains, what was used to restrain the possessed Gerasa man?
    a. handcuffs   b. ropes   c. rings   d. large stones

14. E Whose idea was it to send the demons into the herd of swine?
    a. Legion's   b. Jesus'   c. the crowd's   d. Peter's

15. E What does Satan not allow many people to understand?
    a. exorcisms   b. God's power   c. the trinity
    d. prayer

16. H What happened to the mute boy when approached by Jesus?
    a. he blasphemed   b. he convulsed
    c. he ran away   d. he screamed

17. **H** Which Old Testament person did Jesus claim to be inspired by the Holy Spirit?

    a. Daniel   b. Micah   c. David   d. Solomon

18. **E** How did Jesus send out the apostles to exorcise the people?

    a. singly   b. two-by-two   c. in groups of four   d. all together

19. **M** In which town's synagogue did Jesus expel the first demon?

    a. Cana   b. Capernaum   c. Jerusalem   d. Bethsaida

20. **E** Why did Jesus not allow the demons to speak?

    a. they knew him   b. they blasphemed   c. they scared people   d. they were liars

21. **M** How many swine became possessed by demons?

    a. 200   b. 500   c. 2,000   d. 5,000

22. **E** Who will never be forgiven if he blasphemes against the Spirit?

    a. the apostles   b. those baptized   c. the Pharisees   d. anyone

23. **E** According to Jesus, what would be used to expel demons?

    a. wisdom   b. knowledge   c. his name   d. Scripture

24. **E** What is mentioned first in Mark: the Spirit, angels, Satan, or John the Baptist?

    a. the Spirit   b. angels   c. Satan   d. John the Baptist

25. **H** Where was the woman's possessed daughter when Jesus cured her?

    a. on the street   b. in the temple   c. in a cave   d. in bed

26. E Who performed the first exorcism in Mark?
      a. Peter   b. James   c. Jesus   d. John the Baptist
27. M Which angel is mentioned by name?
      a. Gabriel   b. Raphael   c. Michael   d. none
28. H Where did the possessed Gerasa man usually injure himself?
      a. in the mountains   b. in tombs   c. a and b
      d. in his home
29. M What did the possessed mute boy do after he fell to the ground?
      a. he fainted   b. he rolled around
      c. he cursed God   d. he choked himself
30. E How long had the mute boy been possessed?
      a. 6 months   b. 2 years   c. since childhood
      d. since birth
31. M What happened to the body of the possessed boy when he had seizures?
      a. it became rigid   b. it became limp
      c. it became cold   d. it became white
32. E Who was Jesus with in the desert when Satan tempted him?
      a. angels   b. wild beasts   c. John the Baptist
      d. a and b
33. M What first happened to account for Jesus' reputation spreading throughout Galilee?
      a. baptism   b. a prophecy
      c. an angelic appearance   d. an exorcism
34. M What did the possessed Gerasa man not want Jesus to do?
      a. torture him   b. expel him   c. ridicule him
      d. reveal him

35. **H** Who accused Jesus of being possessed by the devil?
    a. the Romans   b. Pontius Pilate
    c. the scribes   d. other demons

36. **E** What did John the Baptist baptize with?
    a. the Spirit   b. water   c. oil   d. none of these

37. **M** What did the apostles need to successfully cure the possessed mute boy?
    a. command   b. prayer   c. fasting and prayer
    d. they did not

38. **M** When did the possessed Gerasa man usually scream?
    a. daytime   b. nighttime   c. during dreams
    d. continuously

39. **E** Which former demon-possessed person was first to see the risen Jesus?
    a. Mary Magdalene   b. Bartimaeus
    c. Simon the leper   d. Philip

40. **E** By which name is the devil commonly known?
    a. Beelzebub   b. Satan   c. Lucifer
    d. Prince of Darkness

41. **M** How many times is the name "Lucifer" mentioned in Mark's Gospel?
    a. once   b. twice   c. three times   d. not once

42. **E** What did the apostles preach as a prerequisite to exorcisms?
    a. forgiveness   b. faith   c. repentance   d. love

43. **E** God once said, "You are my beloved __ __."
    a. people   b. Son   c. hope   d. Spirit

44. **E** To whom does the lawless age belong?
    a. the Pharisees   b. all sinners
    c. angelic beings   d. Satan

45. E Who foretold of the Holy Spirit's coming?
    a. Elijah   b. John the Baptist   c. Jesus   d. Moses

46. H Where had the swine been when the demons entered them?
    a. on a mountain   b. the desert   c. a cave
    d. a field

47. H How many times is Jesus precisely asked to perform an exorcism?
    a. once   b. twice   c. six times   d. not once

48. H Where did the last exorcism in Mark's Gospel take place?
    a. Jerusalem   b. Gerasa   c. Galilee
    d. location not given

49. M When did the possessed Gerasa man usually injure himself?
    a. daytime   b. nighttime   c. on the Sabbath
    d. continuously

50. E Which vision caused the possessed mute boy to go into convulsions?
    a. Jesus   b. the apostles   c. Gehenna
    d. Judgment Day

51. E With which kind of evil spirit was the boy with the foaming mouth possessed?
    a. hateful   b. mute   c. lustful   d. deceitful

52. H How many times is the Holy Spirit mentioned before the call of Peter?
    a. once   b. twice   c. three times   d. four times

53. E In Jesus' first exorcism, what did the possessed man do when he was freed?
    a. he fainted   b. he quivered   c. he choked
    d. he ran off

54. **M** What could no longer restrain the possessed man at Gerasa?
    a. the crowds   b. ropes   c. chains   d. three men
55. **M** What makes Satan not endure?
    a. hatred   b. dissension   c. jealousy   d. lying
56. **E** Who told the crowds about the demons entering the swine?
    a. the possessed man   b. Jesus
    c. Peter and John   d. the swineherds
57. **H** In which chapter of Mark does the first exorcism occur?
    a. 1   b. 2   c. 3   d. 5
58. **M** What was the name of the mute boy that Jesus cured?
    a. Simon   b. Silas   c. John   d. his name is not given
59. **M** What was needed to drive out the possessed mute boy's spirit?
    a. prayer   b. fasting   c. repentance   d. a and b
60. **H** By what other name did Jesus refer to the spirit of the mute boy?
    a. foul spirit   b. deaf spirit   c. evil spirit   d. Satan
61. **M** Which exorcism story comes first: the synagogue demoniac or the one at Gerasa?
    a. the synagogue demoniac   b. Gerasa
    c. both appear together   d. only Gerasa appears
62. **M** How many times is the name *Gabriel* mentioned?
    a. once   b. twice   c. three times   d. not once
63. **H** Which does Mark's Gospel mention last: demons, angels, Satan, or the Spirit?
    a. demons   b. angels   c. Satan   d. the Spirit

64. E What did the possessed Gerasa man do to show his strength?
 a. he smashed walls   b. he crushed people
 c. he lifted boulders   d. he broke chains

65. E Who expelled most of the demons?
 a. Jesus   b. John the Baptist   c. Peter
 d. all twelve apostles

66. E What came out of the mouth of the possessed mute boy?
 a. blasphemies   b. disease   c. blood   d. foam

67. E How did Jesus heal the possessed mute boy?
 a. prayer   b. command   c. baptism
 d. he did not heal him

68. E As which living thing does the Holy Spirit descend?
 a. a raven   b. a bluebird   c. a dove   d. a swallow

69. M In which town did Jesus first encounter a possessed man?
 a. Capernaum   b. Nazareth   c. Cana   d. Jerusalem

70. M What did Jesus say to the first demon that talked to him?
 a. "Satan!"   b. "You evil one!"
 c. "You foul spirit!"   d. "Be quiet!"

71. E Who did Jesus meet immediately after leaving the boat near Gerasa?
 a. an angel   b. a possessed man   c. Satan
 d. a deaf-mute

72. E "How can _____ expel _____?"
 a. Jesus, Satan   b. God, Satan   c. Satan, Satan
 d. man, Satan

73. **H** Where did demons fling themselves down at Jesus' feet?
   a. the Sea of Galilee   b. the River Jordan
   c. Bethany   d. Tyre
74. **M** What was the reaction of the Gerasa crowd to the healed demoniac?
   a. hatred   b. joy   c. fear   d. indifference
75. **H** What was the nationality of the possessed woman's daughter whom Jesus healed?
   a. Greek   b. Roman   c. Idumean   d. Samaritan
76. **E** What kind of fire does Gehenna possess?
   a. white   b. invisible   c. purifying
   d. unquenchable
77. **E** What did the crowds think after the exorcism of the mute boy?
   a. he was dead   b. he was not cured
   c. he was sickly   d. he was still dangerous
78. **M** When did Jesus first baptize with the Spirit?
   a. after John's arrest   b. after the temptation
   c. when entering Galilee   d. time not given
79. **M** What does Mark mention first: the Spirit, angels, Satan, or demons?
   a. the Spirit   b. angels   c. Satan   d. demons
80. **M** Who was with Jesus when he accused Satan of entering Peter?
   a. Nicodemus   b. a Samaritan
   c. the other Apostles   d. Mary Magdalene
81. **E** From where did Jesus come to be baptized in the Spirit?
   a. Jerusalem   b. Bethlehem   c. Nazareth
   d. Bethany

82. E What did the demon of Jesus' first exorcism do?
   a. shrieked   b. cursed   c. hid   d. threatened

83. M How many demons possessed the man from Gerasa?
   a. 1   b. 12   c. dozens   d. hundreds

84. M Where was the home of "Legion"?
   a. Bethany   b. Capernaum   c. Gerasa
   d. the Decapolis

85. H In which territory did Jesus exorcise the demon of a young daughter?
   a. the Decapolis   b. Galilee
   c. Tyre and Sidon   d. Perea

86 M How many times does John the Baptist mention the Holy Spirit?
   a. once   b. twice   c. three times   d. not once

87. M From what did Jesus expel his first demon?
   a. child   b. man   c. woman   d. house

88. H In which city did Jesus demand to know a demon's name?
   a. Capernaum   b. Cana   c. Bethany   d. Gerasa

89. H How did the possessed man of Gerasa frequently injure himself?
   a. with stones   b. with fire   c. with chains
   d. he bit himself

90. H How many exorcism narratives are found in Mark?
   a. 2   b. 3   c. 4   d. 8

91. M What was John the Baptist's main theme in preaching about baptism?
   a. Jesus   b. the Holy Spirit   c. repentance
   d. a and b

92. **M** How soon after coming out of the water did Jesus receive the Spirit?
    a. immediately   b. after he prayed
    c. when the Baptist left   d. after the temptation

93. **M** Who can carry away the Word of God meant for man?
    a. Satan   b. Jesus   c. the Pharisees   d. Lucifer

94. **E** What power was given to the apostles in order to expel demons?
    a. discernment   b. authority   c. the Holy Spirit
    d. wisdom

95. **E** Which person was strong enough to tame the possessed Gerasa man?
    a. Peter   b. a guard   c. a stone worker   d. no one

96. **E** At Gerasa, who wanted to enter the boat with Jesus as he was leaving the area?
    a. Peter and Andrew   b. Mary Magdalene
    c. the possessed man   d. some Pharisees

97. **E** Who helped the possessed mute boy to his feet?
    a. his father   b. Andrew   c. Jesus   d. no one

98. **M** What are the first two words Jesus said to a demon?
    a. "Unclean spirit"   b. "Be quiet!"
    c. "Be gone!"   d. "Evil being"

99. **E** Which demon in Mark's Gospel is given a personal name?
    a. Rufilius   b. Raphael   c. Legion   d. none

100. **E** What was a prerequisite for Jesus receiving God's Spirit?
    a. John's death   b. the Temptation
    c. his baptism   d. his age

Prophecy
Old and New

1. **E** To whom did Isaiah refer when he said, "Clear him a straight path"?
   a. Jesus   b. John the Baptist   c. the Spirit   d. Joseph

2. **E** "No prophet is without honor except in his _____."
   a. own town   b. present life   c. own mind   d. after life

3. **H** To which Old Testament prophet does Jesus refer: "Empty is the reverence they do me"?
   a. Jeremiah   b. Isaiah   c. Obadiah   d. Malachi

4. **M** To whom did Jesus say that a dead child was only asleep?
   a. Herod Antipas   b. the Roman centurion   c. Philip   d. the crowds

5. **E** Who prophesied, "Be constantly on the watch!"?
   a. John the Baptist   b. the Pharisees   c. Jesus   d. an angel

6. **E** In Mark's Gospel, where was the first prophecy fulfilled?
   a. the River Jordan   b. upper Galilee   c. Nazareth   d. Egypt

7. **M** Where did the Baptist speak his last prophecy?
   a. in Jericho   b. the River Jordan
   c. in Bethsaida   d. Mochareaus

8. **E** Who predicted that Jesus would rise again?
   a. Peter   b. John   c. Jesus   d. Pontius Pilate

9. **M** In the end times, who will come to impersonate Jesus?
   a. Elijah   b. Enoch   c. Satan   d. many people

10. **H** Which event immediately followed the transfiguration?
    a. the coming of Elijah   b. the resurrection
    c. an exorcism   d. a curse

11. **M** To whom did Jesus reveal the coming tribulation?
    a. Pontius Pilate   b. the apostles
    c. Mary Magdalene   d. Joseph of Arimathea

12. **H** To whom did Jesus say, "You are not far from the reign of God"?
    a. Peter   b. a Sadducee   c. a scribe
    d. Nicodemus

13. **E** What did Pontius Pilate prophesy about?
    a. Elijah's return   b. the resurrection
    c. Jerusalem's fall   d. nothing

14. **M** Where did Jesus first prophesy?
    a. Judea   b. Galilee   c. heaven   d. Samaria

15. **E** Whose prophecy does Jesus quote about the "abomination of desolation"?
    a. Daniel's   b. Isaiah's   c. Jeremiah's   d. Ezekiel's

16. **E** Who will shorten the tribulation period?
    a. Satan   b. those in prayer   c. the Lord
    d. Michael

17. **H** What was Jesus' third prophecy about?

    a. the end times   b. universal salvation
    c. the resurrection   d. heaven

18. **H** Where did Jesus mention his fourth prophecy?

    a. Capernaum   b. Bethany   c. Cana   d. Nazareth

19. **E** In the end times, who will fathers hand over to die?

    a. their fathers   b. their wives   c. their sons
    d. their enemies

20. **H** To whom did Jesus prophesy about eternal marriage?

    a. the Sadducees   b. the Pharisees
    c. the apostles   d. Mary Magdalene

21. **M** In which village did Jesus predict that a colt awaited him?

    a. Cana   b. Jerusalem   c. Jericho   d. Bethany

22. **E** According to Jesus, when will be the time of fulfillment?

    a. no one knows   b. at Jesus' baptism
    c. at the resurrection   d. now

23. **M** "Let me (Jesus) assure you, _____ has already come."

    a. Elijah   b. the Baptist   c. Judgment   d. Moses

24. **M** Where did Jesus disclose his second prophecy?

    a. Capernaum   b. Cana   c. the Sea of Galilee
    d. the River Jordan

25. **M** Who is the second man in Mark's Gospel to prophesy?

    a. Isaiah   b. the Baptist   c. Jesus   d. Simeon

26. **E** What did Jesus prophesy about marriage in the afterlife?
    a. you are forever married   b. only angels marry
    c. all those not married will marry
    d. people won't marry
27. **M** Over which issue did Jesus resort to quoting Moses?
    a. the burning bush   b. the Commandments
    c. life after death   d. wanderings
28. **M** Who mentioned Isaiah the prophet's name?
    a. Peter   b. John the Baptist   c. Jesus   d. Satan
29. **E** Who is the "messenger" of Isaiah's prophecy?
    a. John the Baptist   b. Jesus   c. an angel
    d. Joseph
30. **H** Who is the first male prophet mentioned in Mark?
    a. Jeremiah   b. Isaiah   c. Daniel   d. the Baptist
31. **E** What did Jesus say was "at hand"?
    a. power   b. gifts   c. God's reign   d. the tempter
32. **H** To how many apostles did Jesus reveal the coming of Elijah?
    a. 1   b. 2   c. 3   d. 12
33. **M** In the last days, what celestial thing will be shaken?
    a. heavenly hosts   b. the stars   c. the moon
    d. the vaults
34. **E** Which town had trouble accepting the prophecies of Jesus
    a. Capernaum   b. Nazareth   c. Jerusalem   d. Cana
35. **E** In the end times, where did Jesus say earthquakes will occur?
    a. Israel   b. Egypt   c. the East   d. many places

36. E Jesus said, "They will use my name to _____ demons."
    a. confuse   b. entice   c. destroy   d. expel
37. M To which Old Testament prophet did Jesus refer about honoring your parents?
    a. Moses   b. Elijah   c. Isaiah   d. Jeremiah
38. M Who did Jesus predict would flog him?
    a. the scribes   b. the chief priests
    c. the Gentiles   d. Pontius Pilate
39. E Which Old Testament prophet did Satan quote during the temptation?
    a. Isaiah   b. Malachi   c. Samuel   d. none
40. M What Old Testament prophet did Jesus quote at the temptation?
    a. Isaiah   b. Moses   c. Ezekiel   d. none
41. H Where was the last prophecy told in Mark?
    a. Nazareth   b. Bethany   c. Tyre   d. it doesn't say
42. M Who is the first prophet mentioned in the first verse of Mark's Gospel?
    a. Jesus   b. Isaiah   c. the Baptist   d. Elijah
43. M Who is the first prophet in Mark's Gospel to be quoted?
    a. the Baptist   b. John the Apostle   c. Jesus
    d. Isaiah
44. H Which Old Testament prophet does Jesus echo in speaking of disregard for the Commandments?
    a. Malachi   b. Moses   c. Isaiah   d. Daniel
45. M Who is the first prophet mentioned in Mark?
    a. Jesus   b. Isaiah   c. John the Baptist
    d. Jeremiah

46. E Where was the first prophecy heard in Mark?
   a. Jerusalem   b. Babylon   c. the River Jordan
   d. Cana

47. M Who heard the last prophecy in Mark?
   a. the Apostles   b. Martha   c. Jairus
   d. Bartimaeus

48. M Where did the last prophecy by an angel occur?
   a. the tomb   b. Emmaus   c. Damascus
   d. Bethany

49. E What did Nicodemus prophesy about?
   a. Elijah's return   b. Jesus' healings
   c. the resurrection   d. nothing

50. H To whom did Jesus reveal the future coming of Elijah?
   a. Peter   b. James, John   c. Peter, James, John
   d. the Twelve

51. E "Things are hidden only to be _____."
   a. destroyed   b. revealed   c. protected
   d. abused

52. E "Sit at my right hand, until I make your enemies your _____."
   a. victors   b. footstool   c. friends   d. domain

53. H Where did Jesus give his last prophecy in Mark?
   a. Emmaus   b. Bethany   c. Jerusalem
   d. a dinner table

54. M Who is the last prophet mentioned in Mark?
   a. the Baptist   b. Isaiah   c. Moses   d. Jesus

55. M Where did Jesus' prophecy of raising a dead child to life occur?
   a. the synagogue official's house
   b. the centurion's house   c. the tombs
   d. Peter's house

56. **M** Who is the second Old Testament prophet mentioned in Mark?

    a. Micah   b. Isaiah   c. Moses   d. the Baptist

57. **M** Who told the last prophecy in Mark?

    a. Peter   b. Jesus   c. an angel
    d. John the Apostle

58. **E** If the Lord didn't shorten the tribulation, who would be saved?

    a. only Israel   b. only believers   c. a remnant
    d. no one

59. **M** "Anyone who curses his father or mother must be _____."

    a. tortured   b. put to death   c. punished
    d. forever damned

60. **M** "_____ will indeed come first and restore everything."

    a. Enoch   b. the Baptist   c. the Spirit   d. Elijah

61. **E** Where did John the Baptist appear prophesying?

    a. the desert   b. Jerusalem   c. Mount Horeb
    d. the Sea of Galilee

62. **E** "The Son of Man has not come to be served but to _____."

    a. preach   b. baptize   c. rule   d. serve

63. **H** From which Old Testament book does Jesus quote about the patriarch's God?

    a. Genesis   b. Exodus   c. Deuteronomy
    d. Judges

64. **M** According to Jesus, what will be taken someday from the apostles?

    a. their money   b. the dove   c. the groom
    d. their power

65. E What will "pass away" during the last days?
   a. evil   b. the heavens and the earth
   c. worship   d. repentance

66. M "The time is ripe for _____."
   a. Satan's dominion   b. salvation   c. harvest
   d. the tribulation

67. E According to Jesus, who will first come to restore everything?
   a. Michael   b. Satan   c. Enoch   d. Elijah

68. E How long after his death did Jesus say he would rise?
   a. 1 day   b. 2 days   c. 3 days   d. 1 week

69. E Where did Jesus prophesy about stones being torn down?
   a. the marketplace   b. a tower   c. a house
   d. the temple

70. E In the last days, who will young children turn against?
   a. the widowed   b. other children
   c. their parents   d. the elderly

71. M What type of women will have difficult times during the tribulation?
   a. elderly   b. pregnant   c. sick   d. single

72. E Near which city did the prophecy of Jesus' entry come to pass?
   a. Jerusalem   b. Bethlehem   c. Jericho
   d. Bethsaida

73. M Who would spit on Jesus, according to his own prophecy?
   a. the Gentiles   b. the chief priests
   c. the scribes   d. the Sadducees

74. **M** According to Jesus' prophecy, where was he called to preach?

a. Capernaum   b. Jerusalem   c. Nazareth
d. all the villages

75. **M** On the way to Jerusalem, to whom did Jesus predict he would first be handed over?

a. chief priests   b. scribes   c. Pontius Pilate
d. a and b

76. **H** How many times did the Baptist mention Isaiah's name?

a. once   b. twice   c. three times   d. not once

77. **E** In the end times, who will brothers try to execute?

a. their fathers   b. their sisters   c. their friends
d. their brothers

78. **M** What season does Jesus say will be hard for all in the end times?

a. summer   b. winter   c. fall   d. spring

79. **H** Who is the first woman in Mark's Gospel to prophesy?

a. Mary Magdalene   b. Martha
c. the Virgin Mary   d. the hemorrhaged woman

80. **E** Where did the Baptist first prophesy?

a. the River Jordan   b. Jerusalem
c. the Dead Sea   d. Jericho

81. **M** Who is the second man in Mark's Gospel to hear a prophecy?

a. the Baptist   b. Simeon   c. Jesus   d. Peter

82. **M** What prophecy did Jesus reveal to Satan during the temptation?

a. the resurrection   b. Satan's fall
c. God's kingdom   d. none

83. **M** What belief did Jesus encourage in his first prophecy?
    a. humanity   b. the Spirit   c. the Gospel
    d. the Son

84. **M** What was Jesus' second prophecy about?
    a. the crucifixion   b. God's kingdom
    c. discipleship   d. Satan's power

85. **H** What was Jesus' fourth prophecy about?
    a. forgiving sins   b. discipleship
    c. heaven   d. Satan's reign

86. **M** Which prophecy in Mark directly precedes the Last Supper story?
    a. Isaiah's prophecy   b. Peter's denial
    c. Judas' betrayal   d. the fig tree

87. **M** Which prophecy comes after the call of the first apostles?
    a. Satan's fall   b. becoming disciples
    c. God's reign   d. the temptation

88. **M** Where did the first man prophesy?
    a. Samaria   b. the River Jordan   c. Jerusalem
    d. it doesn't say

89. **E** What did Caiaphas prophesy about in Mark?
    a. the resurrection   b. Jerusalem's fall
    c. the crucifixion   d. nothing

90. **M** What was the last prophecy by an angel?
    a. the heavenly banquet   b. the crucifixion
    c. Satan's fall   d. the resurrection

91. **H** Where did Jesus reveal his third prophecy?
    a. Jerusalem   b. the desert
    c. the Sea of Galilee   d. Nazareth

92. **M** Besides Jesus, who prophesied during the temptation?

a. Peter   b. the Baptist   c. Satan   d. no one

93. **H** Which prophecy comes right before the cursing of the fig tree?

a. the resurrection   b. the end times
c. finding a colt   d. the Baptist's death

94. **H** Which prophecy directly follows the Passover preparation?

a. Peter's denial   b. Judas' betrayal
c. Isaiah's prophecy   d. the crucifixion

95. **E** What did Satan prophesy about during Jesus' temptation?

a. Satan's power   b. the Baptist   c. Jesus' reign
d. none

96. **H** What did Martha prophesy about?

a. Jerusalem's fall   b. the resurrection
c. Jesus' healings   d. nothing

97. **M** Which prophecy follows the prophecy about future discipleship?

a. spreading the good news   b. Satan's fall
c. Joseph's death   d. the crucifixion

98. **H** Which prophecy comes immediately after John the Baptist's death?

a. the crucifixion   b. the Spirit's coming
c. God's reign   d. Jesus' power

99. **H** Which prophecy follows the prophecy about Elijah's return?

a. the crucifixion   b. Enoch's return
c. Gabriel's return   d. judgment day

100. **H** To how many apostles did Jesus reveal the coming tribulation?

a. 1   b. 4   c. 11   d. 12

Nature
Earth, Animals, Air

1. **E** Which voice first came out of the desert?
   a. Satan's   b. a serpent's   c. the Baptist's
   d. Jesus'

2. **H** What item had the apostles forgotten about when Jesus stilled the waters?
   a. the wine   b. the fish   c. the loaves   d. the wind

3. **E** Who mentioned huge stones being torn down?
   a. a Pharisee   b. Jesus   c. Caiaphas
   d. Pontius Pilate

4. **M** In which parable do the birds build their nests?
   a. the leaven   b. the seed   c. the yeast
   d. the mustard seed

5. **E** With which plant did Jesus get upset?
   a. an olive tree   b. a shrub   c. a fig tree   d. none

6. **H** How many of the poor widow's coins were made of copper?
   a. 1   b. 2   c. 6   d. none

7. **M** Jesus said, "There will be _____ and there will be famine."
   a. earthquakes   b. floods   c. disease   d. thunder

8. **H** Where did Jesus teach the parable of the seed?
   a. on the water   b. near the water
   c. on a mountain   d. in the desert

9. **M** According to Jesus, what never dies in hell?
    a. vultures   b. worms   c. wolves   d. snakes
10. **M** In the parable of the tenants, where was the victim dragged?
    a. into the vineyard   b. outside the vineyard
    c. to the cave   d. to the sea
11. **E** What kind of food were the apostles allowed to take on missionary journeys?
    a. bread   b. meat   c. grain   d. none
12. **E** What did the apostles untie before they entered Jerusalem?
    a. a colt   b. a camel   c. a dog   d. a fox
13. **M** On the Sabbath, which part of the grain did the apostles pull?
    a. the heads   b. the stalks   c. the roots
    d. the whole grain
14. **E** Which animal part did Jesus first mention in Mark's Gospel?
    a. tail   b. teeth   c. skins   d. ears
15. **E** According to Jesus, which tree's sap will be a sign for the last times?
    a. pine   b. olive   c. oak   d. fig
16. **E** Which color was Jesus "mocked" with?
    a. white   b. purple   c. brown   d. red
17. **E** An apostle said, "Teacher, look at the huge blocks of _____."
    a. stone   b. ice   c. wood   d. salt
18. **H** Which natural earth formation is first mentioned in Mark?
    a. a rock   b. a river   c. a desert   d. a mountain

19. **E** Before Jesus entered Jerusalem, what did the people spread on the road?

    a. perfume   b. reeds   c. thorns   d. flowers

20. **M** From where did God's voice come at the transfiguration?

    a. the mountain   b. the cloud   c. the bush   d. the thunder

21. **E** In the end times, to where must those of Judea flee?

    a. underground   b. another country   c. the desert   d. the mountains

22. **E** Which animal drowned?

    a. a sheep   b. swine   c. a dove   d. a mule

23. **H** On which earthly formation did Jesus decide on the twelve apostles?

    a. a desert   b. a lake   c. a mountain   d. a plain

24. **E** With what was Jesus struck on the head?

    a. a reed   b. a stone   c. a branch   d. iron

25. **H** What was the monetary value of the poor widow's coins?

    a. a few cents   b. a talent   c. a denarius   d. nothing

26. **M** How many loaves of bread did the apostles have for the four thousand?

    a. 2   b. 3   c. 5   d. 7

27. **M** Before feeding the five thousand, the apostles said, "We have five loaves and _____ fish."

    a. 2   b. 3   c. 5   d. 12

28. **E** Jesus said that in hell, "Everyone will be salted with _____."

    a. fire   b. brimstone   c. bitter herbs   d. acid

29. **E** According to Jesus, which natural object could the apostles move with total faith?

    a. a boulder   b. a mountain   c. a whale   d. a lion

30. **E** To which element of nature did Jesus say, "Quiet! Be still!"?

    a. thunder   b. the clouds   c. the rain   d. the sea

31. **M** In the desert, Jesus was with wild _____.

    a. wolves   b. beasts   c. ravens   d. vultures

32. **M** Who mentioned the "burning bush"?

    a. Pontius Pilate   b. a Pharisee   c. Peter   d. Jesus

33. **H** What did Jesus find on the fig tree?

    a. leaves   b. worms   c. birds   d. figs

34. **H** How many fish did the apostles have to feed the four thousand?

    a. 2   b. 4   c. 5   d. a few

35. **E** Who first appeared in the desert?

    a. the Baptist   b. Jesus   c. Satan   d. Peter

36. **M** What was sacrificed on the day of unleavened bread?

    a. a lamb   b. a dove   c. a dog   d. an ox

37. **M** What natural condition does Jesus compare earthquakes to?

    a. storms   b. hurricanes   c. labor pains   d. winter

38. **H** Which animals are first mentioned after the cursing of the fig tree?

    a. colts   b. birds   c. swine   d. dogs

39. **H** What natural object is in a story directly preceding the temple clearing?

    a. a palm tree   b. fish   c. a fig tree   d. a vine

40. **M** Jesus said, "[In hell], everyone will be _____ with fire."

   a. yeast fed   b. quenched   c. salted   d. rotted

41. **E** During the tribulation, what will occur to "know that summer is near"?

   a. people dying   b. mountains falling
   c. rivers drying   d. leaves blooming

42. **H** To whom did Jesus mention the burning bush?

   a. the Pharisees   b. the Sadducees
   c. the apostles   d. no one

43. **H** Where would it be better to go if one leads astray simple believers?

   a. the sea   b. the desert   c. the earthly fires
   d. the crevasses

44. **E** Which workers of nature did Jesus first encounter?

   a. farmers   b. fishermen   c. hunters
   d. none of these

45. **H** In the seed parable, what is not mentioned: thorns, roots, birds, or worms?

   a. thorns   b. roots   c. birds   d. worms

46. **M** Jesus pitied the five thousand because they were like what?

   a. poor doves   b. lost ravens   c. lost sheep
   d. blind mules

47. **H** At what time of day did Peter see the withered tree?

   a. early morning   b. noon   c. late afternoon
   d. early evening

48. **H** According to Jesus, what living thing is used as an example for the "master's coming"?

   a. a serpent   b. a crow   c. a dove   d. a raven

49. **H** What did the Pharisees insist on doing before they ate the market food?
    a. pray over it   b. wash it   c. sprinkle it
    d. enflame it
50. **E** What nonhuman living substance did Jesus curse?
    a. a fig tree   b. a colt   c. a fish   d. none
51. **M** What seed is the earth's smallest?
    a. olive   b. mustard   c. fig   d. wheat
52. **H** Who was the first person mentioned to have eaten bread?
    a. Jesus   b. Jesse   c. Peter   d. David
53. **E** Where did the Spirit first send Jesus?
    a. to a mountain   b. to the desert
    c. to a cave   d. to a cliff
54. **H** During the tribulation, what must the man in the field not retrieve?
    a. his sword   b. his cloak   c. his food   d. his gold
55. **H** What is the last physical animal or creature to be mentioned in Mark's Gospel?
    a. a lamb   b. a spider   c. a snake   d. a wolf
56. **H** In the parable of the tenants, what was put around the vineyard?
    a. weeds   b. a reed   c. trees   d. a hedge
57. **E** Jesus said, "Not _____ stone(s) will be left upon another."
    a. one   b. any   c. two   d. three
58. **H** Which animal or creature did Jesus first mention?
    a. a dog   b. a sheep   c. a wolf   d. a bird
59. **H** In the seed parable, which is mentioned first: birds, roots, sun, or thorns?
    a. birds   b. roots   c. sun   d. thorns

60. **E** Before Christ's entry into Jerusalem, which animal did the apostles procure?
    a. a camel   b. a colt   c. a fox   d. none

61. **E** Jesus said that to keep peace, "Keep _____ in your hearts."
    a. a quiet wind   b. fire   c. honey   d. salt

62. **M** What is the first natural "sign of the times" that Jesus predicted?
    a. floods   b. famine   c. earthquakes   d. disease

63. **E** Which tree did Jesus use as an example for the tribulation and end times?
    a. palm   b. olive   c. fig   d. oak

64. **H** Where was the crowd when Jesus taught them the parable of the seed?
    a. on a mountain   b. in the valley
    c. in the desert   d. on the shore

65. **H** From which areas did some of the multitude that followed Jesus come?
    a. Sidon   b. Transjordan   c. Idumea
    d. all of these

66. **E** Who baptized repenters with water?
    a. John the Baptist   b. Jesus   c. Simeon
    d. a and b

67. **M** What were the second workers of nature that Jesus encountered?
    a. fishermen   b. farmers   c. hunters
    d. none of these

68. **M** Jesus said, "There will be earthquakes and there will be _____."
    a. wars   b. famine   c. floods   d. disease

69. **H** How many apostles procured a colt for Jesus?
    a. 1   b. 2   c. 3   d. all of them

70. **M** For what did Jesus say, "The Master needs it but he will send it back here at once?"
    a. fish   b. bread   c. a colt   d. a dove
71. **M** What heavenly sign did Jesus give the Pharisees?
    a. manna   b. a flock of doves   c. multiple fish   d. none
72. **M** What did Jesus do to the loaves before feeding the five thousand?
    a. he spoke to them   b. he changed them
    c. he distributed them   d. he broke them
73. **M** To which natural condition does Jesus compare famine?
    a. disease   b. labor pains   c. storms   d. winter
74. **E** What kind of honey did John the Baptist eat?
    a. wild   b. bitter   c. manna   d. prepared
75. **H** In the seed parable, which is mentioned last: birds, sun, roots, or thorns?
    a. birds   b. sun   c. roots   d. thorns
76. **M** What were the first animals infested by demons?
    a. dogs   b. wolves   c. swine   d. sheep
77. **H** What word of nature does *Boanerges* mean?
    a. sons of thunder   b. sons of light
    c. sons of water   d. sons of the sun
78. **M** According to Jesus, what will be the onset of labor pains?
    a. earthquakes   b. famine   c. disease   d. a and b
79. **M** Who asked Jesus about the temple's huge blocks of stone?
    a. Nicodemus   b. Caiaphas   c. a Pharisee
    d. an apostle

80. E To what did Jesus say, "Never again shall anyone eat of your fruit"?

   a. an olive tree   b. a vine   c. a fig tree
   d. a grain field

81. E To what animal did Jesus compare the entry to heaven?

   a. a camel   b. a dove   c. a sheep   d. a lion

82. H Who first noticed the withered fig tree?

   a. James   b. John   c. Peter   d. Philip

83. H According to Jesus, which natural element would be a clue for deciding the location of the Last Supper?

   a. water   b. fire   c. gold   d. silver

84. M Which body part did Jesus witness being cut off?

   a. a head   b. an arm   c. a leg   d. an ear

85. M What came over the apostles' boat?

   a. the wind   b. the waves   c. rain   d. fish

86. M Who waited on Jesus during the temptation?

   a. Satan   b. the Spirit   c. animals   d. angels

87. E In which kind of body of water did the Baptist do his work?

   a. a pond   b. the sea   c. a lake   d. a river

88. M Where did Jesus sit when he taught about the signs of the end times?

   a. Mount Hebron   b. Mount Nebo
   c. the Mount of Olives
   d. the Garden of Gethsemane

89. E Jesus said, "Not one _____ will be left upon another."

   a. cloud   b. tree   c. victory   d. stone

90. **M** In which type of country did the first preaching in Mark's Gospel occur?
    a. desert   b. plains   c. valleys   d. highlands
91. **M** Which physical need did Jesus feel when he left Bethany?
    a. food   b. water   c. friendship   d. love
92. **H** What was the colt near that the apostles procured?
    a. a well   b. the water   c. a stable   d. a gate
93. **E** What split in two immediately following Jesus' baptism?
    a. a river   b. a mountain   c. the sky   d. a rock
94. **M** In which part of nature did the apostles witness Jesus' authority?
    a. the sea   b. the wind   c. the sun   d. a and b
95. **H** What covered the fig tree that Jesus approached?
    a. clouds   b. foliage   c. soot   d. figs
96. **M** Why did Jesus not find figs on the fig tree?
    a. it was damaged   b. it was cursed
    c. it was gone   d. it was not ripe
97. **M** Of which type of wood was Jesus' cross made?
    a. pine   b. oak   c. cedar   d. it doesn't say
98. **M** To what did the Canaanite woman leave her leftover food?
    a. vultures   b. dogs   c. swine   d. sheep
99. **M** Of what kind of metal were the widow's coins?
    a. silver   b. gold   c. copper   d. bronze
100. **H** In Mark's longer ending, which living creature is mentioned?
    a. a dragonfly   b. a wolf   c. a serpent   d. a spider

The Passion

1. **M** Besides the unleavened bread, which feast hastened Jesus' trial?
   a. Manna   b. Jubilee   c. Sabbath   d. Passover

2. **H** The perfume poured on Jesus' head was worth how many pieces of silver?
   a. 30 pieces   b. 100 pieces   c. 300 pieces   d. 500 pieces

3. **E** What other name did Jesus use for the location of the Last Supper?
   a. guest room   b. basement   c. dining room   d. house of Zion

4. **M** According to Jesus, what type of men would arrest him?
   a. evil   b. boastful   c. powerful   d. murderous

5. **H** What did Jesus tell his disciples to do at Gethsemane while he prayed?
   a. listen   b. sit down   c. pray together   d. disperse

6. **H** At Gethsemane, how often did Jesus ask the disciples if they were sleeping?
   a. once   b. twice   c. three times   d. not once

7. **E** What place/name did accusing bystanders call Peter after Jesus' trial?
   a. Judean   b. Galilean   c. Nazarean   d. Samaritan

8. **E** With which kind of prisoners was Barabbas linked?
   a. murderers   b. thieves   c. idolaters
   d. treasoners

9. **E** How was the crown of thorns made?
   a. it was twisted   b. it was strung
   c. it was woven   d. it was natural

10. **M** Who claimed, "Clearly this was the Son of God"?
    a. Nicodemus   b. the centurion
    c. Joseph of Arimathea   d. John

11. **M** How many times is Jesus' name mentioned on the inscription above the cross?
    a. once   b. twice   c. three times   d. not once

12. **M** Who did Jesus predict would flog him?
    a. Pontius Pilate   b. the Jews
    c. Herod Antipas   d. the Gentiles

13. **M** Who sent Judas to the Garden of Gethsemane?
    a. the priests   b. the scribes   c. the elders
    d. a, b, and c

14. **H** Who told Jesus to "play the prophet"?
    a. Caiaphas' followers   b. Pilate's followers
    c. Herod's guards   d. no one

15. **M** What came first: the crown of thorns or the scourging?
    a. crown of thorns   b. scourging
    c. both together   d. it doesn't say

16. **H** Who did Pilate ask if Jesus was really dead?
    a. Nicodemus   b. the centurion
    c. Joseph of Arimathea   d. a soldier

17. **E** Besides hitting Jesus, what else did Caiaphas' followers do?
    a. they spit on him   b. they stripped him
    c. they lied to him   d. they crowned him

18. **E** The first question Pilate asked Jesus dealt with which subject?

    a. divinity   b. holiness   c. law-breaking
    d. kingship

19. **M** What was the Praetorium?

    a. a room   b. a hall   c. a court   d. patio

20. **E** Who does Jesus first question on the cross?

    a. God   b. the thief   c. the Virgin Mary   d. John

21. **E** What was the wine offered to Jesus on the cross drugged with?

    a. myrrh   b. palm oil   c. Eastern herb   d. poison

22. **E** How many people at the Last Supper drank the cup of wine?

    a. 3   b. 4   c. 10   d. all of them

23. **E** In Simon's house, where was Jesus when a woman poured perfume on him?

    a. in the bedroom   b. on a bed   c. at a table
    d. on a mat

24. **M** What was used at Gethsemane to cut off the slave's ear?

    a. a knife   b. a sword   c. a wire   d. a rock

25. **H** By which other name does Caiaphas refer to God when questioning Jesus?

    a. Yahweh   b. Abba   c. Blessed One
    d. the Holy One

26. **M** According to Jesus, how many times would Peter hear the cock crow?

    a. once   b. twice   c. three times   d. four times

27. **E** Which kind of wine was Jesus offered on the cross?

    a. salty   b. bitter   c. sweet   d. sour

28. H Which name does Mark give to the eve of the Sabbath?
    a. Jubilee   b. Day of Atonement
    c. Preparation Day   d. Early Sabbath

29. E Who released Barabbas from prison?
    a. Caiaphas   b. Pilate   c. Herod Antipas
    d. the crowds

30. H By which title did the high priest's servant girl call Jesus?
    a. Messiah   b. King of the Jews
    c. Jesus of Nazareth   d. the Nazarene

31. M Where did Jesus go immediately after the Last Supper?
    a. Jerusalem   b. Mount Nebo
    c. the River Jordan   d. the Mount of Olives

32. E Who took Jesus down from the cross?
    a. Joseph of Arimathea   b. Nicodemus
    c. Peter   d. John

33. E Pilate asked Jesus, "Are you the _____ of the Jews?"
    a. king   b. savior   c. anointed   d. hope

34. M Who said, "All hail! King of the Jews!"?
    a. Caiaphas   b. Roman soldiers   c. Pilate
    d. Herod Antipas

35. H Who said, "He saved others but he cannot save himself"?
    a. the priests   b. the scribes   c. the crowds
    d. a and b

36. E On which issue did Peter disagree with Jesus?
    a. the resurrection   b. the crucifixion
    c. the denial   d. Judas Iscariot

37. **E** How was the linen acquired that the dead Jesus was wrapped in?
    a. borrowed   b. bought   c. made   d. stolen
38. **M** Besides saluting, how did the soldiers mockingly honor Jesus after they crowned him?
    a. they kissed him   b. they genuflected
    c. they hugged him   d. they bowed
39. **H** Who was the mother of James the Younger?
    a. Mary   b. Martha   c. Jezebel   d. Salome
40. **E** At which part of the day did darkness fall on the countryside?
    a. early morning   b. midafternoon
    c. late afternoon   d. early evening
41. **E** From which area was the man who helped Jesus carry his cross?
    a. Alexander   b. Antioch   c. Cyrene   d. Jerusalem
42. **E** What was the Jewish sentence for blasphemy?
    a. whipping   b. burning   c. prison   d. death
43. **M** In addition to the chief priests, which Jewish group tried to arrest Jesus?
    a. the ancients   b. the scribes
    c. the Sadducees   d. the Pharisees
44. **E** Which animal was commonly sacrificed on the first day of Unleavened Bread?
    a. a goat   b. a lamb   c. two doves   d. a partridge
45. **E** Who prepared the Passover supper for Jesus?
    a. Martha   b. Caiaphas   c. Mary Magdalene
    d. the apostles
46. **H** What was Jesus doing when Judas appeared to betray him?
    a. weeping   b. sleeping   c. speaking   d. praying

47. **E** Where in Gethsemane did Jesus pray to the Father?
    a. in a tree   b. in the water   c. in the air
    d. on the ground

48. **M** What is the first word Jesus spoke on the cross?
    a. sabachthani   b. lama   c. eloi   d. Elijah

49. **H** Who was Rufus' and Alexander's father?
    a. Simon of Cyrene   b. Rufus   c. Zebedee
    d. Theophilus

50. **E** What did the mockers of Caiaphas ask Jesus to play?
    a. a king   b. a prophet   c. a foreigner   d. God

51. **H** What group made up the Sanhedrin?
    a. the chief priests   b. the elders and scribes
    c. the Pharisees   d. a and b

52. **E** In what color did the soldiers dress Jesus?
    a. black   b. scarlet   c. purple   d. green

53. **E** Which distinguished Jewish group was Joseph of Arimathea from?
    a. the Sanhedrin   b. the Zealots
    c. the Essenes   d. the council

54. **H** According to Mark, what time was Jesus crucified?
    a. 9:00 a.m.   b. 12:00 p.m.   c. 3:00 p.m.
    d. not given

55. **E** Who asked Jesus if he were a king?
    a. Caiaphas   b. Caesar   c. Pilate   d. Herod

56. **M** "Let the Messiah, the _____, come down from that cross!"
    a. Anointed One   b. King of Israel   c. Christ
    d. Son of God

57. **M** Where were Jesus and his disciples going when he first predicted the Passion?
    a. Nazareth   b. Capernaum   c. Jerusalem   d. Cana

58. **E** What was Jesus' burial linen called?
    a. a syndon   b. a veil   c. a cloak   d. a shroud

59. **E** What did Jesus call the bread of the Last Supper?
    a. his body   b. his soul   c. his image
    d. his strength

60. **E** By which name did Jesus refer to Judas Iscariot?
    a. evil one   b. false apostle   c. Satan   d. betrayer

61. **M** How many times does the crowd shout, "Crucify him!"?
    a. once   b. twice   c. three times   d. not once

62. **M** How many times did the cock crow before Peter first remembered Jesus' prediction of denial?
    a. the first   b. the second   c. the third
    d. the fourth

63. **M** What did members of Caiaphas' court do immediately before hitting Jesus?
    a. they crowned him   b. they dressed him
    c. they blindfolded him   d. they cursed him

64. **H** Where had Simon been when he was asked to carry Jesus' cross?
    a. the lake   b. Pilate's court   c. home
    d. the country

65. **H** According to Mark's Gospel, how many women were present at the crucifixion?
    a. 1   b. 2   c. 3   d. it doesn't say

66. **E** How many days would Jesus need to rebuild the temple?
    a. 1 day   b. 3 days   c. 1 week   d. 12 days

67. **M** At Gethsemane, how long was Peter asleep when Jesus awoke him?

    a. 1 hour   b. 3 hours   c. 6 hours   d. all night

68. **E** By what other name did Jesus address his Father at Gethsemane?

    a. Abba   b. Father   c. Eli   d. Alpha

69. **M** To whom did Jesus first speak in Gethsemane after he prayed?

    a. Thomas   b. Peter   c. Martha   d. Judas

70. **E** Which disciple first told Jesus he would never lose faith?

    a. Peter   b. James   c. John   d. Philip

71. **M** Which woman poured perfume on Jesus' head?

    a. Martha   b. Mary Magdalene   c. Anna
    d. it doesn't say

72. **E** The chief priests wanted to arrest Jesus and to _____.

    a. imprison him   b. mock him   c. desert him
    d. kill him

73. **E** In which part of the house was the Last Supper to take place?

    a. upstairs   b. ground level   c. basement
    d. backyard

74. **M** During the Last Supper, which came first: the breaking or blessing of the bread?

    a. breaking   b. blessing   c. neither
    d. it doesn't say

75. **M** What did the young man wear who followed Jesus out of Gethsemane?

    a. a bloody robe   b. expensive jewels
    c. nothing   d. a linen cloth

76. **M** How many separate times did Pilate question Jesus?
    a. once   b. twice   c. three times   d. four times

77. **M** Who asked Jesus, "Have you no answer to what these men testify against you"?
    a. a bystander   b. a soldier   c. the high priest   d. Pilate

78. **E** Who gave the crowds a chance to free Jesus?
    a. Herod   b. Caiaphas   c. Caesar   d. Pilate

79. **H** Who briefly greeted Jesus as "Rabbi"?
    a. Judas   b. Thomas   c. Peter   d. James

80. **E** What does the wine of the Last Supper symbolize?
    a. fear   b. love   c. evil   d. blood

81. **E** To which source did Jesus attribute his knowledge of the Passion?
    a. the scribes   b. the Scriptures   c. Pilate   d. the apostles

82. **E** Jesus said, "My God, my God, why have you _____?"
    a. lied to me   b. deceived me
    c. punished me   d. forsaken me

83. **M** Which came first: the crowning with thorns or the dressing of Jesus with a cloak?
    a. crowning with thorns   b. dressing
    c. both together   d. it doesn't say

84. **E** Who was surprised that Jesus died so soon?
    a. Peter   b. Herod   c. Pilate
    d. Joseph of Arimathea

85. **H** What did Judas warn Jesus' arresters?
    a. use precaution   b. hurry   c. be silent
    d. use weapons

86. **E** By pouring perfume on Jesus' head, the woman was anticipating _____.
    a. Jesus' death   b. Jesus' burial
    c. Jesus' resurrection   d. Jesus' kingdom

87. **E** How many of Jesus' disciples denied that they planned to betray him?
    a. 1   b. 2   c. 3   d. all of them

88. **M** Where did the disciples go immediately after Jesus' arrest?
    a. to Caiaphas' house   b. to Pilate's court
    c. home   d. it doesn't say

89. **H** Besides Peter and John, to whom did Jesus confide his agony at Gethsemane?
    a. Bartholomew   b. Philip   c. James   d. Matthew

90. **M** How many disciples went to look for the place of the Last Supper?
    a. 1   b. 2   c. 3   d. all of them

91. **H** What was the ingredient in the perfume that was poured on Jesus' head?
    a. gum oil   b. nard   c. cottonseed oil
    d. date juice

92. **E** What other name did Jesus use for the Last Supper?
    a. the Jubilee   b. the Bar Mitzvah
    c. the Passover   d. the Sabbath

93. **E** The owner of the house of the Last Supper could be identified by _____.
    a. a vineyard   b. a donkey   c. a sword
    d. a water jar

94. **E** What did Jesus say was near at Gethsemane?
    a. the crucifixion   b. Pilate's death
    c. the resurrection   d. a betrayer

95. E At Gethsemane, what did Jesus tell Peter human nature was?
    a. corruptible   b. true   c. weak   d. strong

96. M By which name did Jesus call those who would mock and kill him?
    a. Gentiles   b. Romans   c. outsiders
    d. Samaritans

97. M When did Joseph of Arimathea arrive at the crucifixion?
    a. early morning   b. late afternoon
    c. early evening   d. midnight

98. H Who was the mother of Joses?
    a. Salome   b. Martha   c. Jezebel   d. Mary

99. M What did Jesus say to Caiaphas about being the Messiah?
    a. "I am"   b. "If you say I am"   c. "I am not"
    d. he was silent

100. H Who asked Jesus if he was the Son of the Blessed One?
    a. a bystander   b. Pilate   c. a soldier
    d. the high priest

From Heaven Above
God, Heaven, and Prayer

1. **H** To whom did Jesus recite the story of Adam and Eve?
    a. the apostles   b. the scribes
    c. the Sadducees   d. the Pharisees
2. **H** In which verse does Mark first mention God?
    a. 1   b. 3   c. 6   d. 12
3. **H** What is the final reference in Mark: heaven, resurrection, or eternity?
    a. eternity   b. resurrection   c. heaven
    d. none of these
4. **E** After what would the rich man have treasure in heaven?
    a. repenting   b. selling his possessions
    c. forgiving   d. dying
5. **E** To what does Jesus compare a "ripe harvest"?
    a. the Spirit   b. Kingdom of God
    c. all repenters   d. himself
6. **M** Which parable explains the most about God?
    a. the seed   b. the mustard seed
    c. the tenants   d. a and b
7. **M** Which group challenged Jesus about the resurrection?
    a. the Sadducees   b. the Pharisees
    c. the Zealots   d. the Herodians

8. **M** Which theme directly precedes Jesus' burial: God, heaven, or prayer?

   a. God   b. heaven   c. prayer   d. a and c

9. **E** Who shouted at Jesus, "You are the Son of God"?

   a. Peter and Andrew   b. unclean spirits
   c. Joseph of Arimathea   d. Nicodemus

10. **M** Which theme in Mark does Jesus address first: God, heaven, or prayer?

    a. God   b. heaven   c. prayer   d. a and c

11. **M** Besides the Baptist, who first acknowledged Jesus as being from God?

    a. Peter   b. Mary   c. Joseph   d. an evil spirit

12. **E** According to Jesus, what is impossible for man but not for God?

    a. miracles   b. forgiveness   c. salvation   d. truth

13. **M** According to Jesus, what will some people see before they taste death?

    a. the Antichrist   b. the judgment day
    c. God's kingdom   d. a great conversion

14. **E** Which body part is better to discard than to miss God's kingdom?

    a. the hand   b. the eye   c. the tongue   d. the foot

15. **H** What is the last chapter in Mark that speaks about heaven?

    a. 13   b. 14   c. 15   d. 16

16. **M** How many times does the Baptist mention the word *God*?

    a. once   b. twice   c. three times   d. not once

17. **H** Who accused Jesus of blasphemy for acting in God's authority?

    a. the scribes   b. the Pharisees
    c. the Sadducees   d. the crowd

18. **H** Which parable explains the least about God?
    a. the mustard seed   b. the seed
    c. the tenants   d. none
19. **E** How many times does Pilate refer to heaven?
    a. once   b. twice   c. three times   d. not once
20. **H** What withered when Jesus said, "Put your trust in God"?
    a. a hand   b. a fig tree   c. a bank account
    d. a field
21. **E** To whom did Jesus refer when he said, "for the Kingdom of God belongs to such as these"?
    a. children   b. the poor   c. the oppressed
    d. the orphaned
22. **E** Where did Jesus first appear to preach about God's reign?
    a. Egypt   b. Judea   c. Galilee   d. Samaria
23. **H** Which term does Jesus use for "a gift devoted to God"?
    a. Eli   b. Corban   c. talitha   d. sabachthani
24. **H.** Which theme directly follows the temptation?
    a. heaven   b. the Spirit   c. prayer   d. God's reign
25. **H** Where does the last talk about God occur?
    a. Bethany   b. Jerusalem   c. Cana
    d. it doesn't say
26. **M** Who did Jesus first accuse of disregarding God's commandments?
    a. the Romans   b. the Sadducees
    c. the scribes and Pharisees   d. Judas
27. **H** According to Jesus, who was not far from God's reign?
    a. a Sadducee   b. a scribe   c. a Zealot   d. Martha

28. **M** Jesus said to the Twelve, "Unto you it is given to know the _____ of the kingdom of God."

   a. mystery   b. fullness   c. beginning   d. sign

29. **E** Which house was Jesus' "house of prayer"?

   a. heaven's abode   b. Peter's house
   c. Jesus' house   d. the Temple

30. **M** Which subject does Jesus address before the Sanhedrin: prayer, heaven, or God?

   a. prayer   b. heaven   c. God   d. b and c

31. **H** Which kind of evil spirit needed prayer to be driven out?

   a. mute and deaf   b. foul   c. lustful   d. none

32. **M** How many postresurrection appearances are mentioned in Mark 16:9-19?

   a. 7   b. 2   c. 3   d. none

33. **M** What does the risen Jesus talk more about?

   a. heaven   b. evangelism   c. prayer   d. God

34. **E** Jesus said, "Reform your lives and believe in the _____."

   a. the Baptist   b. gospel   c. prophet   d. law

35. **E** Jesus said, "Let no man separate what _____ has joined."

   a. the Spirit   b. heaven   c. God   d. love

36. **H** Which is the first prophet mentioned who refers to the Lord?

   a. the Baptist   b. Isaiah   c. Jeremiah   d. Jesus

37. **E** When we stand to pray, what should we do?

   a. forgive   b. repent   c. cleanse ourselves
   d. tell no one

38. **M** Jesus said, "After I am _____, I will go to Galilee ahead of you."
    a. handed over   b. anointed   c. raised up
    d. crucified
39. **M** At the temptation, how many times did Satan mention *God*?
    a. once   b. twice   c. three times   d. not once
40. **H** Where does the last discourse on heaven occur?
    a. Cana   b. Emmaus   c. Capernaum
    d. location not given
41. **H** Which is the last chapter in Mark that talks about God?
    a. 16   b. 17   c. 18   d. 20
42. **H** Where did Jesus repeat the story of Adam and Eve?
    a. by the Mediterranean   b. across the Jordan
    c. Idumea   d. the Decapolis
43. **M** Who called Jesus the "Holy One of God"?
    a. the Baptist   b. Nicodemus   c. an evil spirit
    d. Gabriel
44. **M** Who did Jesus first warn not to reveal his relationship with God?
    a. James   b. the Baptist   c. a leper
    d. unclean spirits
45. **E** To whom did Jesus say he would not drink of the vine for some time?
    a. the apostles   b. the Herodians   c. Martha
    d. Mary Magdalene
46. **E** To whom does Jesus most often teach prayer?
    a. the apostles   b. Martha   c. Nicodemus
    d. Joseph

47. E What do we need to believe to receive in prayer?
    a. that we are blessed   b. that we are forgiven
    c. that we will receive   d. that we are loved

48. M Which is the first heavenly visitor to appear in Mark?
    a. the Father   b. the Spirit   c. an angel   d. Elijah

49. E Which theme in Mark is addressed first: God, heaven, or prayer?
    a. God   b. heaven   c. prayer   d. a and c

50. H Which person was the last to mention the word *God* in Mark?
    a. the centurion   b. Jesus   c. Peter   d. Mary

51. H Who had entered God's house in the days of Abiathar?
    a. Solomon   b. Jesse   c. David   d. Samuel

52. E What did God say to John the Baptist?
    a. Come after me   b. My beloved John
    c. You are my prophet   d. nothing

53. H Which parable in Mark encourages prayer?
    a. the seed   b. the mustard seed
    c. the tenants   d. none

54. M Which theme dominates Mark's last chapter: God, heaven, or prayer?
    a. God   b. heaven   c. prayer
    d. a and c

55. E To what does Jesus compare a mustard seed?
    a. God's reign   b. the Spirit's fruits
    c. faith   d. the seed of love

56. E According to Jesus, which time will be more distressful than any in God's creation?
    a. at Jesus' death   b. the end times
    c. before Jesus dies   d. after Jesus' death

57. **E** Who would not accept the conditions for entry into God's kingdom?
    a. a rich man   b. the Samaritan
    c. a Sadducee   d. a leper

58. **H** Which heavenly theme directly follows Peter's denial?
    a. God   b. heaven   c. prayer   d. a and c

59. **M** How many times does the Baptist mention *heaven*?
    a. once   b. twice   c. three times   d. not once

60. **H** What could allow the "wise" to understand God's reign?
    a. prayer   b. baptism   c. repentance   d. tithing

61. **M** To whom does Jesus teach the Lord's Prayer?
    a. Peter   b. James and John
    c. all twelve apostles   d. Mary and Martha

62. **H** Who was the first person to refer to heaven in Mark?
    a. John the Apostle   b. Jesus   c. God
    d. the Baptist

63. **H** Besides the Pharisees, to whom did Jesus say, "Give to God what is God's"?
    a. the Sadducees   b. the Zealots
    c. the Herodians   d. the scribes

64. **H** Which is the last chapter in Mark that talks about prayer?
    a. 13   b. 14   c. 15   d. 16

65. **H** With reference to the raising of the dead, which Old Testament prophet did Jesus quote?
    a. Moses   b. Isaiah   c. Jeremiah   d. Daniel

66. **H** What does Jesus mean by *corban*?
    a. God's kingdom   b. purity of spirit
    c. bodily desires   d. dedicated to God

67. **E** Which prophet first announces the coming of God's kingdom?

    a. the Baptist   b. Simeon   c. Jesus   d. Micah

68. **M** Which theme directly precedes the blessing of the children?

    a. God   b. heaven   c. prayer   d. faith

69. **H** To whom did Jesus say, "Put your trust in God"?

    a. John the Baptist   b. Nicodemus
    c. the apostles   d. the Samaritan

70. **M** At the temptation, how many times did Satan mention *heaven*?

    a. once   b. twice   c. three times   d. not once

71. **M** To whom did God directly speak when the Spirit descended on Jesus?

    a. the Baptist   b. Jesus   c. Satan   d. the crowd

72. **M** Which theme directly follows the way of the cross: God, heaven, or prayer?

    a. God   b. heaven   c. prayer   d. a and c

73. **E** According to Jesus, how must we accept God's reign?

    a. like the Gentiles   b. like the angels
    c. like children   d. like the Samaritan

74. **E** Jesus said, "With God all things are _____."

    a. renewed   b. true   c. just   d. possible

75. **M** Where does the last discussion of prayer occur?

    a. the Mount of Olives   b. Gethsemane
    c. the temple   d. River Jordan

76. **E** Who at one time was not judging by God's standards but by man's?

    a. Simeon   b. Nicodemus   c. Martha   d. Peter

77. **H** To whom did Jesus call God the "God of the living"?
    a. the Sadducees   b. the Pharisees
    c. the Apostles   d. the Zealots

78. **H** After which event did the crowds first give praise to God?
    a. a baptism   b. a prophecy   c. a cure
    d. Jesus' birth

79. **E** After whose arrest did Jesus preach the reign of God?
    a. Levi's   b. Zebedee's   c. Simeon's
    d. the Baptist's

80. **H** Which parable explains the most about God?
    a. the pearl   b. the good Samaritan
    c. the prayer   d. none of these

81. **H** How does Mark first refer to Jesus?
    a. the Christ   b. the Redeemer
    c. the Son of God   d. the Messiah

82. **H** Who said that Jesus sincerely taught God's way of life?
    a. the Pharisees   b. the Herodians
    c. the Apostles   d. a and b

83. **M** Over which issue did the Jews first accuse Jesus of acting in God's authority?
    a. cleansing the temple   b. a cure
    c. a prophecy   d. forgiving sins

84. **M** How many chapters in Mark are devoted to the risen Christ?
    a. 1   b. 2   c. 3   d. 4

85. **M** Who was the first person to refer to God in Mark's Gospel?
    a. the Baptist   b. Mark   c. Peter   d. Jesus

86. E Who called Jesus "Son of God Most High"?
      a. Nicodemus   b. Martha   c. Lazarus   d. a demon
87. E Jesus said, "At the beginning of creation God made them _____ and _____."
      a. free, perfect   b. male, female   c. Adam, Eve
      d. free, just
88. E Jesus' first words were, "This is the time of _____."
      a. deliverance   b. judgment   c. great promise
      d. fulfillment
89. H Which parable explains the least about heaven?
      a. the seed   b. the mustard seed
      c. the tenants   d. the good Samaritan
90. E What did Jesus demand of the man who wanted eternal life?
      a. forgiveness   b. repentance   c. obedience
      d. selling his possessions
91. M According to Jesus, who failed to understand God's power?
      a. the Herodians   b. the Pharisees
      c. the Zealots   d. the Sadducees
92. H Where was Jesus called the "holy One of God"?
      a. Capernaum   b. Nazareth   c. Cana   d. Jerusalem
93. H Who was the last person to talk about prayer?
      a. Mary Magdalene   b. John the Apostle
      c. Jairus   d. Jesus
94. E Jesus said, "Put your trust in _____."
      a. the Son   b. the Spirit   c. eternal life   d. God
95. E According to Jesus, what is God's "good news"?
      a. Calvary   b. eternal life   c. forgiveness
      d. the reign of God

96. **M** How many times does Judas refer to God?
    a. once   b. twice   c. three times   d. not once
97. **M** Where did Jesus say he would go after he was raised up?
    a. Galilee   b. heaven   c. Jerusalem   d. Damascus
98. **M** What does the risen Christ talk least about: heaven, God, or prayer?
    a. heaven   b. God   c. prayer   d. a and b
99. **E** How many times does Pilate refer to God?
    a. once   b. twice   c. three times   d. not once
100. **M** Which theme dominates Mark's first chapter?
    a. God   b. heaven   c. prayer   d. a and b

General Questions
History and Archaeology

1. When was the Infancy Gospel of Thomas written?
   a. ca. A.D. 50   b. A.D. 100—A.D. 150   c. A.D. 200—A.D. 250
   d. A.D. 300
2. Where was the Gospel of Thomas discovered?
   a. Nag Hammadi   b. Cairo   c. Antioch   d. Ebla
3. Which apocryphal gospel relied heavily upon the Gospel of Matthew?
   a. Gospel of the Hebrews   b. Gospel of the Egyptians
   c. Gospel of Peter   d. Gospel of Philip
4. How many "secret sayings" of Jesus does the Gospel of Thomas record?
   a. 15   b. 34   c. 88   d. 114
5. What does "hai graphai" refer to?
   a. apocrypha   b. Gospel   c. the Scriptures
   d. Testament
6. Where did the Gospels receive their first form of "canonization"?
   a. Rome   b. Jamnia   c. Jerusalem   d. Ephesus
7. Who was first known for his beliefs in Mark being the oldest Gospel?
   a. Gottlob Wilke   b. Heinrich Holtzmann
   c. Karl Lachmann   d. Edward Simons

8. Who was first to indicate that Mark was "Peter's interpreter" and wrote his Gospel accordingly?
   a. Eusebius   b. Origen   c. Papias   d. Tertullian

9. Where did Clement of Alexandria say that Mark carried on his first missionary activity?
   a. Lybia   b. Persia   c. Greece   d. Egypt

10. Who may have killed the apostle Peter?
    a. Nero   b. Calligula   c. Caesar   d. Felix

11. Who has the oldest attested copy of the fourth Gospel?
    a. Ryland's Library   b. Hopkin's Museum
    c. Wilkin's Library   d. the University of Cairo

12. We have the oldest attested copy of which Gospel?
    a. Mark   b. John   c. Matthew   d. Luke

13. Who called the Gospels "the Memoirs of the Apostles"?
    a. Eusebius   b. Justin Martyr   c. Philo   d. Josephus

14. Who was writing when Jesus was alive?
    a. Clement   b. Jerome   c. Seneca   d. Eusebius

15. Who overthrew the Jews in A.D. 70?
    a. Pliny   b. Octavius   c. Josephus   d. Titus

16. From where was Philo (the contemporary of Jesus)?
    a. Alexandria   b. Antioch   c. Susa   d. Athens

17. To where did Jesus send Thaddeus?
    a. Pergamum   b. Rome   c. Edessa   d. Jerusalem

18. In which century were the Gospels first written on parchment?
    a. first   b. third   c. sixth   d. seventh

19. How many centuries elapsed between the original Gospels and our earliest complete copies?
    a. 1   b. 2   c. 3   d. 6

20. How many Greek gospel manuscripts do we possess?
    a. 2   b. 250   c. 640   d. 2,500

21. How many copies of Jerome's Latin Vulgate do we possess?
    a. 0   b. 2   c. 800   d. 8,000
22. In which language are the oldest Gospel text copies traceable?
    a. Greek   b. Aramaic   c. Hebrew   d. Latin
23. How many towers did Herod's palace Antonia have?
    a. 3   b. 1   c. 6   d. 0
24. Who was governor of Syria when Jesus began his public career?
    a. Romulus   b. Quirinius   c. Flaccus   d. Archelaus
25. When did the Jews first revolt against Rome?
    a. 75 B.C.   b. 12 B.C.   c. A.D. 29   d. A.D. 90
26. When did Masada fall?
    a. A.D. 8   b. A.D. 73   c. A.D. 86   d. A.D. 90
27. Which Jewish temple was destroyed in A.D. 70?
    a. the first   b. the second   c. the third   d. the fourth
28. On which side of the temple mount is the wailing wall?
    a. north   b. south   c. east   d. west
29. Which structure is found directly west of the upper city in Jerusalem?
    a. temple mount   b. Antonia fortress
    c. Herod's palace   d. pool of Siloam
30. When did the Essenes first establish themselves near the Dead Sea?
    a. 150 B.C.   b. 36 B.C.   c. A.D. 6   d. A.D. 64

General Questions
Geography

1. How far did the King's Highway extend in Gospel times?
   a. to Antioch   b. to Susa   c. to Tyre   d. to Damascus
2. Why was the Jezreel Valley important?
   a. alluvial soil   b. fruit   c. roadways   d. a and c
3. What was the Negev desert's main population center?
   a. Jerusalem   b. Beer-sheba   c. Shilo   d. Decapolis
4. What kind of land formation is Upper Galilee?
   a. mountain plateau   b. wadi   c. desert   d. swamp
5. Where is the lowest point on earth?
   a. Chorazon   b. Sea of Galilee   c. Gaza   d. the Dead Sea
6. Where is the Arabah district located in Palestine?
   a. the sea coast   b. the hill country
   c. the Jordan rift   d. the slopes
7. In what geographical region are the Sea of Galilee and the Dead Sea found?
   a. Jordan Valley   b. Trans-Jordan   c. the highlands
   d. the coastal area
8. What was the capital of Galilee?
   a. Capernaum   b. Nazareth   c. Tiberias   d. Perea
9. What was Bethsaida also known as?
   a. Paneas   b. Iulias   c. Tyre   d. Moraea

10. What was another name for Caesarea Philippi?
    a. Paneas   b. Iulias   c. Bethsaida   d. Sidon
11. Who was the province of Idumea named after?
    a. Galileans   b. Nazoreans   c. Edomites   d. Itureans
12. How far below sea level is the Sea of Galilee?
    a. 696 feet   b. 35 feet   c. 200 feet   d. 1424 feet
13. What was Magdala?
    a. a country   b. a province   c. a town   d. a mound
14. What was the Sea of Galilee also known as?
    a. Sea of Tiberias   b. Lake of Gennesareth
    c. Sea of Chorazon   d. a and b
15. How long was the well-known road from Jerusalem to Jericho?
    a. 5 miles   b. 14 miles   c. 25 miles   d. 40 miles
16. What color are the hills in the valley of the lower Jordan?
    a. red   b. white   c. black   d. green
17. Which mountain do the Arabs call "the ancient of days"?
    a. Hermon   b. Ararat   c. Zula   d. Olives
18. What color are the hills of Moab?
    a. gray   b. white   c. yellow   d. purple
19. What smell permeates the Dead Sea?
    a. resin   b. sulphur   c. smoke   d. pine
20. How far is the road from Bethsaida to Cana?
    a. 7 miles   b. 18 miles   c. 30 miles   d. 120 miles
21. How far above sea level is Cana?
    a. 85 feet   b. 540 feet   c. 1,640 feet   d. 3,140 feet
22. In Jesus' day, how wide was the province of Galilee?
    a. 30 miles   b. 50 miles   c. 100 miles   d. 500 miles
23. How long was Galilee from north to south in Jesus' time?
    a. 25 miles   b. 30 miles   c. 50 miles   d. 200 miles

24. Where does the main water supply come from in Galilee?
    a. Mediterranean Sea   b. Mt. Ararat   c. Sea of Galilee
    d. Mt. Hermon
25. Which type of fish was not caught by the apostles on the Sea of Galilee?
    a. perch   b. carp   c. pike   d. bass
26. What is the color of the rich alluvial deposit found in the region of Galilee?
    a. red   b. yellow   c. black   d. white
27. What grows abundantly in Galilee?
    a. olives   b. wheat   c. palms   d. all of these
28. Which is the only town on the Sea of Galilee that still has life today?
    a. Capernaum   b. Magdala   c. Tiberias   d. Hippos
29. What is Jericho's mean annual temperature?
    a. 55°F   b. 77°F   c. 98°F   d. 110°F
30. What kind of rock was used in building in the houses of Nazareth in Jesus' time?
    a. limestone   b. granite   c. quartz   d. basalt

General Questions
The Unique and Peculiar

1. Which Gospel most emphasizes miracles?
   a. Matthew b. Mark c. Luke d. John
2. Whose Gospel appears to indicate that Jesus had a three-year public career?
   a. John's b. Matthew's c. Mark's d. Luke's
3. Which Gospel disproportionately emphasizes the passion of Christ?
   a. Luke b. Matthew c. John d. Mark
4. Which Gospel doesn't have a eucharistic institution?
   a. Matthew b. Mark c. Luke d. John
5. Is there a Gospel that mentions no prayer in Gethsemane?
   a. John's b. Matthew's c. Mark's d. Luke's
6. Which evangelist makes the raising of Lazarus a major motivation for the death of Jesus?
   a. Mark b. Luke c. John d. Matthew
7. Which of the Gospels makes no mention of Jesus' preexistence or birth?
   a. Mark b. Luke c. Matthew d. none of these
8. Whose Gospel was probably written shortly after the death of Peter in Rome?
   a. Mark's b. Matthew's c. John's d. Luke's

9. Which Gospel mentions Jerusalem being "trodden down by the Gentiles"?

    a. Matthew's   b. Mark's   c. Luke's   d. John's

10. Which Gospel uses the term *kingdom of heaven* thirty-two times?

    a. Mark   b. John   c. Matthew   d. Luke

11. Which evangelist preferred the expression "kingdom of heaven" over "kingdom of God"?

    a. John   b. Matthew   c. Mark   d. Luke

12. In Mark's Gospel, how many verses in the passion narrative mention Peter?

    a. 0   b. 14   c. 2   d. 22

13. Who among the Gospel writers seems to set down Paul's knowledge of Christ?

    a. Luke   b. John   c. Mark   d. Matthew

14. Who is the most literary of the four evangelists?

    a. Matthew   b. Mark   c. Luke   d. John

15. Which evangelist appears to be the most "cultured"?

    a. Matthew   b. Mark   c. John   d. Luke

16. Which Gospel emphasizes Jesus' ministry in Judea the most?

    a. John   b. Mark   c. Matthew   d. Luke

17. How many visits of Christ to Jerusalem does John's Gospel record?

    a. 1   b. 3   c. 5   d. 0

18. How many visits of Jesus to Jerusalem does each of the synoptic gospels record?

    a. 1   b. 2   c. 3   d. 5

19. How many miracles of Jesus does John mention?

    a. 7   b. 5   c. 12   d. 0

20. How many of Jesus' miracles in John's Gospel are not found in the other Gospels?
    a. 1   b. 5   c. 4   d. 0

21. Whose Gospel was written in a poor and dull form of Greek?
    a. Mark's   b. John's   c. Luke's   d. Matthew's

22. Which Gospel writer uses antithesis and parallels the most?
    a. Mark   b. Luke   c. Matthew   d. John

23. Which two Gospel writers were among the twelve apostles?
    a. Mark, Matthew   b. Luke, John   c. Matthew, John   d. John, Mark

24. What Gospel records the story of Martha and Mary?
    a. Luke   b. John   c. Mark   d. Matthew

25. Which of the Evangelists mentions the word *ecclesia* (church)?
    a. Matthew   b. Mark   c. Luke   d. John

26. Which Gospel deals with the theme of wealth the most?
    a. John   b. Luke   c. Matthew   d. Mark

27. Who was the most apologetic in his Gospel version?
    a. Matthew   b. Mark   c. Luke   d. John

28. Whose Gospel expresses the fear of the people toward Jesus the most?
    a. Matthew's   b. John's   c. Luke's   d. Mark's

29. Which Gospel has the most emphasis on suffering?
    a. Mark   b. Luke   c. John   d. Matthew

30. Which evangelist stresses the hiddenness and secrecy of Jesus Christ's mission the most?
    a. John   b. Luke   c. Mark   d. Matthew

Answers

The Twelve Apostles

Answers

1. b. 1:14
2. b. 1:21
3. b. 2:15
4. a. 6:9
5. d. 3:17
6. a. 10:32
7. a. 13:3
8. d. 9:3
9. d. 8:5
10. c. 6:37
11. d. 14
12. c. 16:18
13. c. 16:14
14. d. 16:5,7
15. a. 14:71
16. c. 9:2
17. d. 9:35
18. a. 11:21
19. a. 1:29
20. c. 2:14
21. b. 3:17
22. b. 5:1
23. a. 6:10
24. c. 10:10
25. d. 11:11
26. a. 9:4
27. a. 8:29
28. d. 16:12
29. b. 16:18
30. c. 14:37–41
31. d. 6:45
32. c. 10:28
33. b. 13:3
34. b. 9:5
35. d. 1:38
36. d. 1:20
37. a. 3:16
38. b. 6:7
39. b. 6:32,35
40. b. 8:29
41. c. 9:5
42. b. 11:1
43. a. 9:32
44. d. 9:5
45. c. 16:14,20
46. d. 16:15
47. a. 16:9–10
48. b. 9:2
49. c. 9:5
50. a. 11:7
51. a. 1:18
52. b. 1:35
53. b. 2:18
54. a. 6:9
55. c. 3:17
56. b. 2:25
57. d. 10:35–37
58. c. 11:14
59. d. 6:31
60. a. 9:7
61. b. 16:20
62. d. 16:14
63. a. 16:12
64. c. 1:21
65. a. 1:36
66. d. 2:15
67. b. 4:38
68. a. 3:17
69. c. 3:9
70. c. 6:12
71. d. 1:23–26
72. b. 1:20
73. c. 1:14
74. d. 4:10
75. d. 9:34
76. c. 8:10
77. b. 8:8
78. c. 9:7
79. d. 10:38–39
80. a. 16:16
81. a. 16:12
82. c. 8:2
83. b. 9:38
84. b. 1:9–11
85. a. 1:19
86. a. 3:13
87. d. 6:8
88. c. 4:38
89. c. 11:11
90. c. 8:33
91. a. 16:17
92. b. 16:11
93. c. 10:35
94. d. 16:19
95. c. 1:29
96. c. 4:35
97. a. 3:13
98. d. 16:10
99. c. 6:51
100. b. 14:19,45

Words of Jesus
Sayings, Parables, Beatitudes

Answers

1. c. 4:1–28
2. a. 4:1
3. d. 4:10
4. a. 12:1
5. b. 4:32
6. b. 4:30–32
7. d. 10:13–16
8. a. 4:30–32
9. a. 15:1–20
10. c. 1:14–15
11. b. 9:46
12. b. 10:25
13. d. 12:1
14. a. 16:17–18
15. b. 4:1
16. d. 12:1
17. a. 4:19
18. b. 2:14
19. d. 12:39
20. a. 12:13–17
21. b. 12:15
22. d. 1:21
23. b. 12:6
24. a. 3:33–35
25. a. 9:48
26. b. 2:22
27. b. 4:30–32
28. a. 12:38
29. c. 4:3
30. b. 4:17
31. c. 12:8
32. d. 4:24
33. a. 15:2
34. c. 6:2
35. b. 12:10–11
36. c. 4:3–28
37. d. 4:9
38. b. 16:17–18
39. a. 7:21
40. d. 9:48
41. d. 4:2
42. b. 4:3
43. a. 4:10
44. b. 12:1
45. a. 4:30
46. c. 12:5
47. d. 1:15
48. c. 1:23
49. d. 3:31–35
50. c. 1:15
51. c. 12:38
52. c. 4:21–22
53. a. 12:12
54. d. 8:15
55. c. 10:23
56. d. 8:15
57. a. 4:1
58. a. 1:14–15
59. c. 12:40
60. d. 4:1–28
61. b. 4:12
62. a. 12:1–11
63. a. 12:40
64. d. 12:1–9
65. c. 11:27–33
66. c. 12:8
67. d. 1:9–11
68. d. 7:15
69. b. 9:50
70. a. 12:17
71. d. 2:25–28
72. d. 16
73. d. 4:35–41
74. a. 14:53–65
75. a. 4:21–22
76. d. 4:27
77. c. 4:8
78. a. 4:30
79. d. 4:4
80. a. 4:34
81. c. 4:32
82. d. 12:2–6
83. c. 4:2
84. d. 15:21–32
85. a. 6:6
86. b. 4:5
87. c. 4:34
88. b. 7:8
89. a. 12:1
90. d. 12:7
91. c. 9:49
92. d. 11:22
93. a. 12:9
94. c. 11:17
95. c. 4:13
96. a. 12:3
97. c. 12:1
98. d. 14:62
99. a. 16
100. d. 1:1–13

Teachings of Jesus
Laws, Morals, Ethics

Answers

1. b. 1:15
2. c. 1:21
3. a. 9:35
4. d. 9:47–48
5. c. 10:19
6. b. 12:26–27
7. d. 10:35–37
8. a. 12:28
9. a. 12:38
10. c. 12:40
11. d. 16:9–20
12. b. 8:36
13. a. 9:1
14. d. 9:30–32
15. b. 9:38,49

16. d. 15:16–20	45. d. 13:33	73. a. 12:38
17. b. 16:15	46. b. 6:34	74. c. 1:16–21
18. a. 1:40–45	47. c. 10:8	75. d. 9:37
19. a. 12:39	48. a. 9:23	76. c. 10:6
20. d. 12:40	49. a. 12:18–25	77. b. 12:30–31
21. d. 12:14	50. d. 12:13–14	78. a. 12:38–40
22. d. 12:18,23	51. c. 9:45	79. b. 13:37
23. c. 10:9	52. d. 10:16	80. d. 8:34
24. d. 10:27	53. d. 7:18	81. c. 9:9–10
25. b. 4:1	54. b. 9:23	82. d. 1
26. c. 8:38	55. c. 1:16–17	83. a. 1:38
27. a. 1:14–15	56. b. 1:23–27	84. c. 7:21–22
28. b. 9:40	57. c. 12:18,27	85. b. 10:23
29. a. 10:10–12	58. a. 10:18	86. d. 15:21–32
30. c. 12:16	59. a. 14:21	87. b. 2:6–11
31. b. 11:22	60. d. 13:21	88. a. 13:28
32. b. 1:22	61. b. 16:9–20	89. d. 8:34
33. d. 1:22	62. b. 12:39	90. c. 10:35–38
34. a. 7:9	63. a. 12:35	91. d. 2:10
35. b. 1:38	64. a. 10:7	92. d. 1:14–15
36. c. 9:43	65. c. 9:38–40	93. a. 1:22
37. b. 10:20–22	66. d. 1	94. c. 2:13–14
38. a. 12:13–15	67. d. 12:13–15	95. c. 14:24
39. c. 10:45	68. a. 9:50	96. d. 13:31
40. d. 12:32–34	69. d. 5:36	97. c. 12:38
41. b. 13:2	70. b. 2:27	98. b. 13:13
42. c. 9:37	71. b. 1:16–17	99. a. 9:38
43. c. 9:2–13	72. d. 1:21	100. b. 1:21–22
44. c. 13:14		

Miracles
Visions, Healings, Appearances

Answers

1. a. 1:10	19. a. 7:31–35	37. b. 2:1–12
2. b. 3:30	20. c. 16:9	38. a. 10:46
3. d. 7:33	21. b. 1:10	39. c. 1:23–28
4. a. 16:5	22. b. 8:22–25	40. b. 5:35–36
5. a. 5:1–13	23. d. 5:42	41. b. 10:46–52
6. b. 1:23–26	24. d. 3:10–11	42. b. 7:31–35
7. a. 2:1–3	25. b. 1	43. a. 1:9–11
8. c. 7:24–30	26. a. 5:21–23	44. d. 5:1–13
9. b. 8:22–25	27. a. 7:31–35	45. a. 1:23–28
10. a. 6:14	28. c. 1:29–31	46. d. 8:20
11. a. 3:1–5	29. d. 1:23–26	47. a. 16:2
12. b. 1:9–11	30. a. 1:9–11	48. a. 1:10
13. d. 4:39	31. c. 6:45–52	49. b. 5:1–13
14. c. 8:19	32. d. 3:13–15	50. b. 5:37–41
15. a. 6:53	33. a. 6:48–50	51. b. 2:11
16. b. 1:32–34	34. d. 1:40–45	52. c. 7:25–30
17. c. 3:1–6	35. d. 3:1–5	53. d. 10:46–52
18. a. 6:13–15	36. c. 6:14	54. d. 2:6

55. a. 6:13
56. b. 3:1–5
57. a. 8:23
58. d. 6:56
59. a. 1:39
60. b. 1:9–11
61. a. 1:23–28
62. d. 5:43
63. b. 5:25–28
64. c. 1:40–44
65. c. 7:24–30
66. a. 1:21–28
67. c. 1:9–11
68. a. 5:25–30
69. c. 3:22
70. b. 7:31–34
71. a. 10:46–51
72. c. 1:10–11
73. a. 16:9
74. b. 6:16
75. d. 2:1–3
76. b. 6:36–44
77. d. 1
78. a. 6:14
79. c. 1:40–45
80. b. 1:45
81. a. 4:39
82. b. 5:22–23
83. b. 6:14–15
84. d. 1
85. a. 5:41
86. d. 5:25–28
87. d. 1:23–26
88. a. 6:16
89. c. 5:30
90. d. 6:48–50
91. b. 8:1–10
92. d. 2:1–5
93. c. 8:11–12
94. d. 8:22–25
95. d. 6:37–44
96. a. 5:25–26
97. d. 8:11–12
98. d. 7:33
99. c. 1:23–26
100. b. 16:9

The Spiritual World
Angels, Demons, The Holy Spirit
Answers

1. a. 1:7–8
2. b. 1:10–12
3. c. 1:21–24
4. d. 1:35
5. b. 5:9
6. a. 5:20
7. b. 16:7
8. d. 9:18
9. b. 9:23–24
10. a. 1:13
11. a. 16:9
12. d. 5:1–20
13. a. 5:4
14. a. 5:11–12
15. b. 16:1–9
16. b. 9:20
17. c. 12:36
18. b. 6:7
19. b. 1:21–23
20. a. 1:34
21. c. 5:13
22. d. 3:29
23. c. 16:17
24. d. 1:4
25. d. 7:30
26. c. 1:23–26
27. d. 16:5
28. c. 5:5
29. b. 9:20
30. c. 9:21
31. a. 9:18
32. d. 1:13
33. d. 1:27–28
34. a. 5:7
35. c. 3:22
36. b. 1:8
37. d. 9:18
38. d. 5:5
39. a. 16:9
40. b. 1:13
41. d. 1:13, 3:22–26
42. c. 6:12–13
43. b. 1:11
44. d. 16:1–9
45. b. 1:7–8
46. a. 5:11–13
47. a. 7:24–30
48. d. 9:14–29
49. d. 5:5
50. a. 9:20
51. b. 9:17–18
52. c. 1:8–12
53. b. 1:26
54. c. 5:3
55. b. 3:26
56. d. 5:14
57. a. 1:23–28
58. d. 9:14–29
59. a. 9:29
60. b. 9:25
61. a. 1:23–28
62. d. 1–16
63. a. 16:17
64. d. 5:4
65. a. 1–16
66. d. 9:18,20
67. b. 9:25
68. c. 1:10
69. a. 1:21–23
70. d. 1:25
71. b. 5:1–2
72. c. 3:23
73. a. 3:7,11
74. c. 5:15
75. a. 7:26
76. d. 9:43
77. a. 9:26
78. d. 1:9–22
79. a. 1:8
80. c. 8:33
81. c. 1:9
82. a. 1:23
83. d. 5:9
84. c. 5:1
85. c. 7:24–30
86. a. 1:8
87. b. 1:23

88. d. 5:1,9
89. a. 5:5
90. c. 1:23–28; 5:1–20; 7:24–30; 9:14–17
91. d. 1:7–8
92. a. 1:10
93. a. 4:15
94. b. 3:14–15
95. d. 5:4
96. c. 5:18
97. c. 9:27
98. a. 5:8
99. c. 5:9
100. c. 1:9–11

Prophecy
Old and New

Answers

1. a. 1:3
2. a. 6:4
3. b. 7:7
4. d. 5:35–39
5. c. 13:33
6. a. 1:1–8
7. b. 1:1–11
8. c. 10:34
9. d. 13:6
10. a. 9:12–13
11. b. 13:3–37
12. c. 12:32,34
13. d. 15:1–15
14. b. 1:14–15
15. a. 13:14
16. c. 13:20
17. b. 1:38
18. a. 2:1–10
19. c. 13:12
20. a. 12:18,25
21. d. 11:1–3
22. d. 1:15
23. a. 9:13
24. c. 1:16–17
25. b. 1:1–8
26. d. 12:25
27. c. 12:23–36
28. b. 1:1–2
29. a. 1:2
30. b. 1:2
31. c. 1:15
32. c. 9:2–8
33. a. 13:25
34. b. 6:1–6
35. d. 13:8
36. d. 16:17
37. a. 7:10
38. c. 10:34
39. d. 1:12–13
40. d. 1:12–13
41. d. 14:62
42. a. 1:1
43. d. 1:2
44. c. 7:6–8
45. b. 1:2
46. c. 1:4–8
47. a. 16:1–8
48. a. 16:5–7
49. d. 1–16
50. c. 9:2–13
51. b. 4:22
52. b. 12:36
53. d. 16:14–18
54. d. 16:6–7
55. a. 5:35–39
56. c. 1:44
57. b. 16:15–18
58. d. 13:20
59. b. 7:10
60. d. 9:12
61. a. 1:4
62. d. 10:45
63. b. 12:26
64. c. 2:20
65. b. 13:31
66. c. 4:29
67. d. 9:12
68. c. 10:34
69. d. 13:2
70. c. 13:12
71. b. 13:17
72. a. 11:11
73. a. 10:34
74. d. 1:38
75. d. 10:33
76. d. 1–16
77. d. 13:12
78. b. 13:18
79. d. 5:25–28
80. a. 1:4–8
81. d. 1:16–17
82. d. 1:12–13
83. c. 1:15
84. c. 1:16–17
85. a. 2:8–10
86. c. 14:17–21
87. b. 1:16–17
88. d. 1:2
89. d. 14–15
90. d. 16:5–7
91. b. 1:35–38
92. d. 1:12–13
93. c. 11:1–3
94. b. 14:17–21
95. d. 1:12–13
96. d. 1–16
97. a. 1:38
98. c. 1:14–15
99. a. 9:31
100. b. 13:3–37

Nature
Earth, Animals, Air

Answers

1. c. 1:3
2. c. 6:51–52
3. b. 13:2
4. d. 4:30–32
5. c. 11:12–14
6. b. 12:42
7. a. 13:8
8. a. 4:1
9. b. 9:48
10. b. 12:8
11. d. 6:7–8
12. a. 11:4–5
13. a. 2:23
14. c. 2:22
15. d. 13:28
16. b. 15:18–20
17. a. 13:1
18. c. 1:3
19. b. 11:8
20. b. 9:7
21. d. 13:14
22. b. 5:13
23. c. 3:13–14
24. a. 15:19
25. a. 12:42
26. d. 8:5
27. a. 6:38
28. a. 9:49
29. b. 11:23
30. d. 4:39
31. b. 1:13
32. d. 12:24–26
33. a. 11:12–14
34. d. 8:7
35. a. 1:4
36. a. 14:12
37. c. 13:8
38. b. 11:15
39. c. 11:12–14
40. c. 9:49
41. d. 13:28
42. b. 12:18–26
43. a. 9:42
44. b. 1:16–17
45. d. 4:3–8
46. c. 6:34
47. a. 11:20–21
48. b. 13:35
49. b. 7:4
50. a. 11:12–14
51. b. 4:31
52. d. 2:25–26
53. b. 1:12
54. b. 13:16
55. c. 16:18
56. d. 12:1
57. a. 13:2
58. d. 4:4
59. a. 4:3–8
60. b. 11:1–4
61. d. 9:50
62. c. 13:8
63. c. 13:28–31
64. d. 4:1
65. d. 3:8
66. a. 1:8
67. a. 1:19–20
68. b. 13:8
69. b. 11:1–2
70. c. 11:1–3
71. d. 8:11–13
72. d. 6:41
73. b. 13:8
74. a. 1:6
75. d. 4:3–7
76. c. 5:11–13
77. a. 3:17
78. d. 13:8
79. d. 13:1
80. c. 11:12–14
81. a. 10:25
82. c. 11:20–21
83. a. 14:13
84. d. 14:45–47
85. b. 4:37
86. d. 1:12–13
87. d. 1:5
88. c. 13:3–4
89. d. 13:2
90. a. 1:4
91. a. 11:12
92. d. 11:4
93. c. 1:9–10
94. d. 4:41
95. b. 11:12–14
96. d. 11:12–14
97. d. 15:21–26
98. b. 7:28
99. c. 12:42
100. c. 16:9–18

The Passion

Answers

1. d. 14:1
2. c. 14:5
3. a. 14:14
4. a. 14:41
5. b. 14:32
6. b. 14:37, 41
7. b. 14:70
8. a. 15:7
9. c. 15:17
10. b. 15:39
11. d. 15:26
12. d. 10:33–34
13. d. 14:43
14. a. 14:65
15. b. 15:15
16. b. 15:44
17. a. 14:65
18. d. 15:2
19. b. 15:16
20. b. 15:34
21. a. 15:23
22. d. 14:23
23. c. 14:3
24. b. 14:47

25. c. 14:61	51. d. 15:1	76. b. 15:2,4
26. b. 14:30	52. c. 15:17	77. c. 14:60
27. d. 15:36	53. d. 15:43 (NIV)	78. d. 15:9
28. c. 15:42	54. a. 15:25	79. a. 14:45
29. b. 15:15	55. c. 15:2	80. d. 14:24
30. c. 14:67	56. b. 15:32	81. b. 14:21
31. d. 14:26	57. c. 10:32	82. d. 15:34
32. a. 15:46	58. d. 15:46	83. b. 15:16–22
33. a. 15:2	59. a. 14:22	84. c. 15:44
34. b. 15:16–18	60. d. 14:42	85. a. 14:44
35. d. 15:31	61. b. 15:13,14	86. b. 14:8
36. c. 14:29–31	62. b. 14:72	87. d. 14:19
37. b. 15:46	63. c. 14:65	88. d. 14:50
38. b. 15:19	64. d. 15:21	89. c. 14:33
39. a. 15:40	65. d. 15:40	90. b. 14:13
40. b. 15:33	66. b. 14:58	91. b. 14:3
41. c. 15:21	67. a. 14:37	92. c. 14:14
42. d. 14:64	68. a. 14:36	93. d. 14:13
43. b. 14:1	69. b. 14:37	94. d. 14:42
44. b. 14:12	70. a. 14:29	95. c. 14:38
45. d. 14:16	71. d. 14:3	96. a. 10:33
46. c. 14:43	72. d. 14:1	97. c. 15:42–43
47. d. 14:35	73. a. 14:15	98. d. 15:40
48. c. 15:34	74. b. 14:22	99. a. 14:62
49. a. 15:21	75. d. 14:51–52	100. d. 14:61
50. b. 14:65		

From Heaven Above
God, Heaven, and Prayer

Answers

1. d. 10:2–6	21. a. 10:14	42. b. 10:1–6
2. a. 1:1	22. c. 1:14	43. c. 1:23–24
3. c. 16:19	23. b. 7:11	44. d. 3:11–12
4. b. 10:21	24. d. 1:14–15	45. a. 14:25
5. b. 4:26–29	25. d. 16	46. a. 11:25; 13:18; 14:32
6. d. 4:1–34	26. c. 7:5–8	47. c. 11:24
7. a. 12:18	27. b. 12:32–34	48. b. 1:9–11
8. a. 15:37–39	28. a. 4:11	49. a. 1:14–15
9. b. 3:11	29. d. 11:17	50. a. 15:39
10. a. 1:14–15	30. d. 14:62	51. c. 2:25–26
11. d. 1:23–24	31. a. 9:25–29	52. d. 1
12. c. 10:26–27	32. c. 16:9–19	53. d. 4,12
13. c. 9:1	33. b. 16	54. a. 16
14. b. 9:47	34. b. 1:15	55. a. 4:30–32
15. d. 16	35. c. 10:9	56. b. 13:19–20
16. d. 1	36. b. 1:2	57. a. 10:21–22
17. a. 2:6–7	37. a. 11:25	58. c. 14:32
18. c. 4:12	38. c. 14:28	59. d. 1
19. d. 15:1–15	39. d. 1:12–13	60. c. 4:11–12
20. b. 11:21–22	40. d. 16	61. d. 1–16
	41. a. 16	62. b. 1:14

63. c. 12:13,17
64. b. 14:32–42
65. a. 12:26
66. d. 7:11
67. a. 1:4
68. a. 10:6–9
69. c. 11:19–22
70. d. 1:12–13
71. b. 1:11
72. a. 15:33–34
73. c. 10:15
74. d. 10:27
75. b. 14:32–42
76. d. 8:33
77. a. 12:18,27
78. c. 2:10–12
79. d. 1:14–15
80. d. 4,12
81. c. 1:1
82. d. 12:13–14
83. d. 2:6–7
84. a. 16
85. b. 1:1
86. d. 5:7–8
87. b. 10:6
88. d. 1:15
89. c. 4,12
90. d. 10:21
91. d. 12:18,24
92. a. 1:21–24
93. d. 14:38–40
94. d. 11:22
95. d. 1:14–15
96. d. 14:10–31
97. a. 14:28
98. c. 16
99. d. 15:1–15
100. a. 1

General Questions

Answers

History and Archaeology
1. b.
2. a.
3. a.
4. d.
5. c.
6. b.
7. c.
8. c.
9. d.
10. a.
11. a.
12. b.
13. b.
14. c.
15. d.
16. a.
17. c.
18. b.
19. c.
20. d.
21. d.
22. a.
23. a.
24. c.
25. d.
26. b.
27. b.
28. d.
29. c.
30. a.

Geography
1. d.
2. d.
3. b.
4. a.
5. d.
6. c.
7. a.
8. c.
9. b.
10. a.
11. c.
12. a.
13. c.
14. d.
15. b.
16. a.
17. a.
18. d.
19. b.
20. b.
21. c.
22. a.
23. c.
24. d.
25. d.
26. a.
27. d.
28. c.
29. b.
30. d.

The Unique and Peculiar

1. b.	11. b.	21. b.
2. c.	12. d.	22. d.
3. d.	13. a.	23. c.
4. d.	14. c.	24. a.
5. a.	15. d.	25. a.
6. c.	16. a.	26. b.
7. a.	17. c.	27. c.
8. a.	18. c.	28. d.
9. b.	19. a.	29. a.
10. c.	20. b.	30. c.